THE TAIL OF THE RACCOON, PART II

TOUCHING THE INVISIBLE

A Scientific Short Story

Barbara Zito
Arthur Tomie, Ph.D.

Book Cover Illustration By
Steven James Petruccio

Published By
ZT Enterprises, LLC

ZT Enterprises, LLC (Publisher), 2014 Licensing Agreement
P.O. Box 2409
Princeton, NJ 08540
Publisher Web site: www.tailoftheraccoon.com
Publisher E-mail: ztenterprisesllc@gmail.com

Library of Congress Cataloging-in-Publication-Data

Barbara Zito, 1958-
Arthur Tomie, 1946-
      The Tail of the Raccoon, Part II: Touching the Invisible /
      by Barbara Zito and Arthur Tomie. Includes Educational
      Commentary, Scientific Commentary, Bibliographical
      References, Glossary.
      ISBN-13: 987-0-9913495-5-5
      ISBN-10: 0-9913495-5-5

INTERIOR DESIGN: Nikyta Sharma
WEBSITE: Kelli Curiotto

PORTIA. Therefore, for fear of the worst, I pray thee, set a deep glass of Rhenish wine on the contrary casket; for, if the devil be within and that temptation without, I know he will choose it.

The Merchant of Venice (Act 1, Scene 2), William Shakespeare

TABLE OF CONTENTS

CHAPTER

One

WORLDS APART

Beside the lapping waters, beyond the mountain ridge, deep in the heart of the Great Forest lived a handsome raccoon called Sign Tracker. Here he lived contentedly; swimming, sleeping, and eating crayfish far removed from the shore where he had been born. Sign Tracker had migrated away from the place of his birth. When the waters ebbed, he had swum across the river to remove himself from the tempting foods of the people. He enjoyed spending time with them and would have liked to remain in their midst, but reminders of their food held sway over his behavior and being near the signs was a danger to him. He knew that he would likely lose control of himself if he stayed in his old haunts and so he had removed himself from the situation. The Lake, the Great Forest, the Earth and the Sky provided everything that Sign

Tracker needed, but something was missing. There was a searching desire hidden within his soul that was slowly awakening.

Beyond the lapping waters, beside a mountain ridge, deep in the heart of the Great Forest stood Mapache in front of his wigwam. Although he had lost the gift of sight, he could clearly picture in his mind the moon beginning to rise above the mountains. He knew that the ripples on the lake where his old friend Sign Tracker lived would soon start to glisten. A narrow band of moonlight would slowly expand across the water, brightening the view. As the moon continued its climb into the night sky, many creatures were falling into repose, soon to be replaced by others who were about to begin their nocturnal wanderings. Mapache's ears were attuned to all of the sounds of the Great Forest. He listened to the gentle chirping of the birds who were settling down for the night. A rustle of leaves, the snapping of a twig, the distant howl of a wolf, nothing escaped his attention. He felt a light breeze brush past his cheeks bringing with it the scent of pine.

Mapache thought of Sign Tracker and asked himself, "Is my old friend watching the moon rise over the waters?" Sign Tracker would surely be roaming the woods right now thought Mapache. He wondered why he had become preoccupied lately with thoughts of this raccoon and the Great Lake. Was something happening which caused his thoughts to stir toward that direction or was this a premonition of things to come? Mapache became convinced that with the changing of the seasons there would soon be a reunion between himself and his old friend. He would enjoy a reunion with that clever character called Sign Tracker because the raccoon could be quite amusing and had shared a meaningful moment in Mapache's life.

Sign Tracker strode along the shores of the lake. It was time to catch some crayfish. His stomach churned with hunger. There were signs of crayfish all around him. Did Sign Tracker notice the ripples on the lake or the moon rising? Not a chance; Sign Tracker was too busy using his nose, hands and eyes to find a juicy meal. At this moment, if the thought didn't involve filling his belly, he wasn't aware of it.

Sign Tracker's nose twitched continuously. He spread his nostrils and drew in deep puffs of air. He tested the moist breeze drifting over the lake while using his nimble hands to search for crayfish. He smelled the mud where the crayfish lay waiting. But there was another, more tantalizing scent that wafted through the air and grabbed his attention. It was the scent of a female raccoon. This female was alluring. His instincts urged him to follow this female. There was no choice for him. He didn't know this particular female, but he was captivated by her already. Her scent drew him near, attracted him and urged him on. Sign Tracker did not realize it, but it was the life inside of him longing to continue that drove his instinct and would result in him finding a mate.

Sign Tracker smiled when he discovered the female within his territory. "What luck!" thought Sign Tracker, "Quite a fortunate fellow am I to behold such a beautiful sight. Now this is a view that I welcome indeed." Delighted was Sign Tracker to have found a hungry female visiting his favorite haunts. He approached her boldly.

"My name is Procyona," she said, coyly introducing herself.

Sign Tracker was instantly charmed by her feminine ways and resolved to do everything in his power to make himself appealing to her. He flexed his muscles and posed in the perfect light in order to show off his handsome physique. Procyona was quite taken by this healthy demonstration of his desire to please her.

Sign Tracker and Procyona spent the next day together. They talked and laughed about silly things - wading in the water and sunning themselves on the shore of the lake. Sign Tracker tried hard to be a perfect gentleman as he knew that his kind attentions would win her confidence. He gave Procyona the choicest crayfish he could find while keeping the smaller ones for himself. He moved rocks out of the way and piled sand together so that she could relax in a comfortable spot on the shore. He was trying very hard to show her his finest qualities while also talking to her gently and keeping a watchful eye over her.

Procyona, though hesitant at first, was charmed by his chivalrous actions. His winning ways convinced her that he would make a fine mate. They spent many joyful evenings sitting close together reclined by the water's edge. Sign Tracker nuzzled Procyona with a powerful tenderness and whispered words of love in her ear. Procyona responded to him with affection and cheerfulness. And so it was that nature drew Sign Tracker and Procyona together beneath the glow of the moonlit skies and they became a mated pair.

CHAPTER
Two

WINTER NIGHTS

During the coldest season of the year the tribal people gathered together to form a large, main winter camp. This was a time when the people could not occupy themselves with outdoor activities and so they gathered inside their wigwams telling stories and playing games. Mapache, the noble warrior who had been blinded in a fierce battle, was the children's favorite storyteller. He would describe in vivid detail the events of days past along with the exploits of renowned individuals. The children would sit around the fire listening closely to each of Mapache's words. They dreamed that what were now merely the entertainments of childhood would one day become the realities of adulthood. The children listened with awe as Mapache explained how great deeds were made possible by the powerful medicine held by their ancestors.

"It is as our forefathers said," spoke Mapache to the children as they huddled together inside his wigwam. Their shadows, cast by the blazing fire, flickered against the walls as gusts of wind buffeted against them. Mapache continued to speak and the little ones soon became pacified by the sonorous tone of his voice.

"The coldest weather occurs when the sun shines, but not a breath of air is stirring. The warrior who encounters the blizzard storm and intense cold will suffer hardships, but there will be many things to instruct and interest him during his travels. Should the warrior be forced to confront the wintry chill of a dead calm, his spirit may not be adequate to the task, and will dissolve, leaving his body still and lifeless in a bank of snow. Many a warrior has perished in a dead calm who would have lived, even thrived, in a blizzard or freezing wind. Hear my words little ones. A warrior may brave the fiercest tempest, only to be defeated by a deadly silence. It is as our forefathers said. Do not be frightened by the raging tempest, as it is the power of the deadly silence that is to be the most feared."

Mapache reassured the children that they would survive the harsh months of winter. The cold weather months were difficult to endure, but the people lived on the food they had gathered and stored during the seasons of harvest. A few hunters, however, traveled into the forest in search of animals whose thick winter coats were greatly prized by the people. The animals had cold weather fur that was full, soft and in prime condition. It was for these furs that the warriors braved the cold and difficult trails into the mountains. When they returned from their winter hunt, the people were reminded that the coldest season of the year was coming to a close.

CHAPTER
Three

—————◆◆◆————

SWEETER THAN HONEY

As the days lengthen, the energy of the sun warms the Great
Forest, preparing the soil to nourish and support the budding
flowers. The smell of new life drifts through the air. The rivers
thaw and rush with melted snow. Trees of all kinds begin to grow
their roots deeper into the earth in order to draw life giving
moisture into the treetops.

For the people, this is the beginning of the season of
abundance. However, it is also a time for hard work, as they must
gather and provision as much food as they can while the season
lasts. Many foods are available only at this particular time of year
and must be gathered and processed in early spring. Of these foods

there was one that the people were particularly fond of, and so, they were willing to work long and hard to produce it. This food was the sugar which was made from the "sweet water" that was tapped from the sugar maple tree.

During the "moon of boiling" the women gathered the sap of the sugar maple into birch bark buckets by making a V-shaped cut into the tree bark and inserting an elderberry stem into the cut to create a tap. The trees, some of which had been thriving for a century, produced many quarts of sweet water. The people built great fires upon which they boiled the sap in large kettles until it thickened and became maple syrup. After this it could be boiled down some more so that when it cooled it would harden into sugar. The people had to be very industrious in order to prepare their sugary treat and they were well suited to this task. After many long hours of collecting the sap and boiling it down, they had a precious supply of maple sugar and syrup which they would use as an ingredient in many of their favorite foods. The syrup was not merely a sweetener, it also contained minerals and vitamins that added to its ability to provide energy.

Very happy were the people with the results of their efforts and after having reaped the rewards of their many hours of labor they would give thanks to the Great Spirit for providing so abundantly. What mother earth had given to the people must now be stored securely underground. The maple syrup and sugar were stored in clay pots and birch bark containers in an underground storage pit lined with rawhide and stone slabs. In this way they stored the precious ingredient far from the noses of the hungry animals of the forest, many of whom have a love of honey and other sweets. And, so it was, that the people carefully hid their maple sugar from the roaming animals, knowing that, given the chance they would surely devour it.

CHAPTER
Four

―――――≫•≪―――――

A NEW LIFE

One evening while Sign Tracker was strolling along the lake's edge looking for crayfish, as was his usual custom, he looked about for Procyona, but she was nowhere to be found. She had gone off on her own without telling him. Sign Tracker sensed that something unusual was happening. He stayed by the shore of the lake in the spot where Procyona often frequented. "Why would Procyona venture into the forest alone?" thought Sign Tracker a bit anxiously. "Surely she is aware of the many dangers lurking in the Great Forest. Where could she be?"

In due time, Procyona did return to Sign Tracker. She appeared one evening as if nothing had happened. As soon as Sign

Tracker heard her familiar footsteps his heart skipped a beat. Procyona was leading a litter of cubs. Sign Tracker had become a father. He approached his new family quizzically because even though he instinctively had an affinity for the cubs, they were something new to him. Procyona greeted Sign Tracker with a quick lick to the snout and then sat up on her haunches, as bears do, to nurse her little ones. Sign Tracker felt a mixture of relief and surprise. Procyona was preoccupied with caring for her cubs. "I should have known," said Sign Tracker happily. "Procyona would not leave me. She has brought me a fine bunch of cubs. Oh, how quickly worry turns to gladness and pain turns to joy in this - this mysterious life of ours."

Sign Tracker was very pleased with his new way of life. Procyona and the precious cubs she had given him opened up a different view of the world. It was a challenging time, but one whose joys, sorrows, and struggles made his life full and interesting. The things that had once been important to him did not seem very important now, in fact, they were somewhat trivial. He had a new set of priorities and a family to feed and defend. He no longer spent his days gathering crayfish in order to feed himself.

Instead, he roamed along the shores of the lake both day and night digging up a variety of edibles for his family.

Though Sign Tracker often grew tired from the many hours of food gathering, the joyful greetings of his cubs when he returned from his travels lightened his heart and lifted his spirits. Their cubby features, playful ways and cheery voices helped him forget about the many hours of toil it took to feed so many hungry mouths. His instincts drove him to provide for and protect his family and fortunately, he was well-suited to the task. Taking care of his family required industriousness, perseverance, patience, resilience, and know-how. He would wade in the water along the lake's edge digging through the mud with his forepaws while singing to himself like this:

"This Life We Have Born"

"I had been Waiting,
For what,
I don't know.
Something was Hidden,
That I wanted to Show."

"When into my Life,
You chose to appear,
Since then I've awakened,
To Springtime all year."

"May the Sun,
That has warmed us.
Reappear every morn,
May it Never be Winter,
In this Life we have Born."

Procyona spent her days caring for her cubs and watching them grow. When the cubs were born they were covered with plain brown fur. It had taken several days for their black masks and the rings on their tails to appear. As they got older their markings increased and the rings on their tails became more distinct. Procyona and Sign Tracker, accustomed to spending moonlit nights together, named their sons after the stars in the heavens; Sirius, Orion, and Lepus. Their daughter was a miniature version of her mother, so naturally, they called her Procilina. Remarkably, their eldest son, Sirius, developed markings on his coat unlike any they had seen on another raccoon. In the direct sunlight his mask took on an unusual tone of purplish black that reminded Sign Tracker of the blackbird's iridescent feathers. These richly colored markings communicated to the world that Sirius was a force to be reckoned with. The middle son, Orion, physically resembled Sign Tracker more than the others. He was quite a handsome raccoon, very much like his father, and was developing a fine looking physique. Lepus, on the other hand, had fewer rings on his tail than his siblings, and his fur was a light gray. He was smaller than his brothers and closer in size to his little sister, Procilina. He was very fond of his sister whose pretty face, melodic voice, and playful nudges never failed to brighten his day. Before long, Procyona was taking the cubs with her on brief food gathering trips. The cubs enjoyed tagging along with their mother and their healthy appetites never slackened.

"This is all I can ask of life," Sign Tracker would say to Procyona, his eyes gazing at her with the look of gleaming obsidian. "To sit here with you in the warmth of the sun, hearing the merry laughter of our cubs and watching them play. To watch the sunlight glisten on the lake - a lake that provides so many crayfish and abundance. Oh, Procyona, if only these days could last forever!"

But life has a way of changing and Sign Tracker's life was no exception. Changes were coming for Sign Tracker's family as the cubs grew older and started to follow their own separate paths. Procyona could sense this. As she and her mate shared those wonderful days, she would be filled with love for him and a fervent longing that these pleasant times would continue endlessly. It was then that she would feel a wave of melancholy overtake her along with the knowledge that one day she would look back on these days wistfully.

CHAPTER
Five

—————————⟫•⟪—————————

VENISON STEW

To the wigwam of Mapache went the young men at the break of dawn. Lately, their hunts had been unsuccessful and they had experienced some mishaps that had discouraged them. The men needed advice from Mapache because even their snares had not caught a rabbit in quite a long while. They knew that Mapache was an expert at crafting traps for all kinds of game. The only success they had recently was with a water trap that had caught a few muskrats, but in the last few weeks their hunting had fallen short and their women and children had grown tired of eating stored food alone. All were looking forward to adding some tasty fresh meat to their stew.

Mapache listened to the concerns of the young men while his fire smoldered. One of them stoked up the fire with a heavy log and some kindling wood. The smoke rose through the smoke hole and drifted into the blue sky. Mapache was very familiar with these types of questions and had heard them many times before. The answer was simple and he answered them thusly, "In order to snare a deer, you must think like a deer. In order to kill a bear, you must think like he does. You must know the habits of your prey and be able to think one step ahead of him. Know the trails that he walks, what he fears and what entices him. But, above all, you must respect the spirit of those you are pursuing. Do as I say and you will have venison always hanging."

Mapache gave a great deal of advice to the young men about the tactics they needed to use when hunting deer, but he held back his advice when it came to devising traps to catch the raccoons. He was fond of the raccoons and felt a brotherhood with them. He and some of the others living in the village remembered Sign Tracker, and Mapache had decided against giving the men any advice on how to trap a raccoon. Thus, their traps weren't quite as effective as they could have been.

Mapache sent the young men on their way, and they promised to bring back a slab of venison from the first deer they snared. They were very intent on being good hunters as they had masculine pride and families to feed. Their women and children would celebrate when they came home with news of fresh venison. All of the families of the village would feast together, singing and laughing as they celebrated their abundance. When all of them had eaten their fill they would become drowsy because of the heaviness of their full stomachs. Eventually, each of them would return to their own blanket to lie down and slumber peacefully in the warmth of the wigwam beside the glow of the fiery embers.

CHAPTER
Six

GOODNESS COMES TO CALL

The family of Sign Tracker grew fast and became strong. The cubs began to roam far and wide as wild animals do as they gain independence. Orion especially was quite a wanderer. He had discovered a stand of fallen trees which made it quite easy to cross the narrowest part of the river. Though he did not know it, this brought him closer and closer to the land of the people. His world had opened up and he was very intent on discovering whatever the Great Forest had to offer.

One day Orion asked Lepus if he would like to join him on an expedition far from home. He promised him an adventure in the world that lay across the river. Lepus usually hung around with his sister Procilina near the lake, but he was eager to do something different and so he decided to tag along with his brother Orion. The two of them climbed trees, waded through streams, poked their noses into rocky crevices and scrounged up a great variety of foods. They weren't very picky eaters and easily made a feast of insects, acorns, and seeds. When they grew tired, they rested together in the hollow of a large tree high above the ground. After a good long rest they resumed their travels along newly forged paths. The two brothers were having a great time, but it was about to get even better. Somehow, by sheer chance, during their meanderings, they had stumbled upon a food storage pit designed by the people. Lepus and Orion had never seen anything like this. It was a storage pit dug into the ground in the shape of a jug and lined with walls of grass and rawhide. A cover made of branches and sticks had a rope attached to it that led down into the earth where the people had stored their maple syrup.

The discovery of the rope and storage pit piqued the interest of both raccoons. Thanks to their nimble fore paws, which very much resembled human hands, they were able to draw the rope up with their dexterous "fingers". They drew the rope up toward them and managed to bring to the surface a tightly sealed clay pot. Orion skillfully used his paws and sharp teeth to pry the top off the vessel without breaking it. Instantly the brothers were overwhelmed by a powerful wave of sweet aroma that flowed across their sensitive nostrils. There it was, a cache of the sweetest food that they had ever tasted. The brothers were beside themselves with delight as they scooped the sticky maple syrup out with their paws and lapped up the exquisite sweetness. Lepus was very impressed by his brother's talents. "You sure were right about this one Orion," said Lepus. "We really found something great this time." "Yumm," mumbled Orion as the thick maple syrup coated his raccoon tongue, "This is even better than honey!" They licked their sticky fore paws clean and got ready to dip in for some more when something told them that they had better pause for a moment. They thought of their father who had warned them against poking their raccoon noses into the people's food. Orion was especially haunted by thoughts of his father's disapproval and muttered to himself like this:

"Father Would Not Like This"

"Father would not like this,
He'd say we crossed the line.
I hear his words - "Resist!"
"I Warned you of the Sign."

"Father would not like this,
He'd say the choice is mine,
To Heed his Words - or Take the Risk,
Now, that's the Bottom Line."

"We had better not eat it all," said Orion, "Come on, let's put this stuff back before we get in big trouble." Lepus was eager to consume every bit of the maple syrup, but he deferred to his brother's wishes. He helped seal the pot back up and the two of them gradually lowered the clay pot back down into the ground. They then carefully covered the storage pit with brush to disguise their intrusion. As they walked away, they knew that they would come back another day for more, but they were not sure when. The brothers had indeed crossed the line, and their recent escapades would set in motion a turn of events that would involve the entire family.

And so it was that the family of Sign Tracker was about to embark on a long and treacherous journey that would take them to a destination that they had never imagined.

CHAPTER
Seven

BROTHERS, BUT DIFFERENT

Lepus and Orion often set out in search of the locations where the people had concealed their delicious food. After having discovered the first cache, Lepus had prodded Orion to explore the forest further until they had learned exactly what to look for so that they could uncover others. Many days they would roam the forest, with Orion taking the lead, looking for any indication that the rope leading into the storage pit was nearby. Each time was much like the last. The brothers would find the rope carefully camouflaged by the people. Then they would use their raccoon "hands" to draw up the rope that was attached to a container of food. Both enjoyed the food immensely and would chow down contentedly. This was a very dangerous occupation, but the brothers were young and naive.

As far as they were concerned, their forest home had become a treasure trove of exotic meals thanks to the resourcefulness of the people.

The need to store food combined with the need for seasonal movement had forced the people to invent methods to preserve food for long periods of time in an ever-changing environment. This suited Orion and Lepus perfectly. The brothers could find caches of sweet treats along trails and clustered together at various sites throughout the forest. The brothers became more ravenous as their rewards consistently increased. They had big appetites which energized their instinct to roam about the forest in search of food. Again and again the brothers enjoyed success in their quest to locate the sweet morsels. Sniffing out the sweets had become much easier for them since they had discovered a pattern of storage pits along well-worn trails within a familiar area. Over and over again Lepus pulled up the rope and found something delicious to eat at the other end. He became so practiced in the art of acquiring the sweet treats that he began to pull up the rope in record time.

Orion knew that there was something very wrong with their

thievery, but mentioning the need to slow down did not dissuade Lepus from his single-minded pursuit of the sweet treats. Orion, on the other hand, hesitated a bit when they came upon the people's food because he remembered his father's warnings, and deep inside he knew that it would be best to heed them. Nevertheless, the two brothers would sit side by side, leaning back on their haunches with their tails helping to balance them, as they indulged in the pleasure of stuffing their mouths full of the sweetened morsels.

The brothers reacted very differently to the rope that led into the storage pit. Lepus was riveted by the sight of the rope and much more driven than Orion to approach the rope once he caught sight of it. While Orion would cautiously approach the place where the food was hidden, Lepus would race over to the rope and lunge for it without a moments hesitation. The rings on the tail of Lepus were quickly fading as he became unable to resist the impulse to lick and chew on the rope that symbolized the delicious food. Although they had become more adept at finding the hidden cache, their attempts to reach the sweets were ruined when this very peculiar impulse began to overwhelm Lepus. His frantic movements had become more intense after each encounter with the sweet treats. Orion's attempts to get to the cache of food were thwarted because Lepus would run for the rope and chew on it so vigorously that it would snap in half and fall to the bottom of the pit before Orion could do anything to prevent it. Ultimately, as soon as the rope came into view, the more sensible Orion was shoved aside by the impetuous Lepus whose bizarre impulses won the day, but lost the sweets, once again.

Oftentimes, Orion would lash out at Lepus in exasperation. "What is wrong with you Lepus? Let go of the rope," demanded Orion. "Can't you control yourself? You ruined everything. Why are you chewing on the rope like that! Get a hold of yourself!"

Lepus seemed unable to control the impulse that he had to approach the rope, grab onto it and start to chew on it as if it were food. His behavior had gotten so out of control that he had begun to chase after things that merely resembled the rope. When he saw a vine hanging from the limb of a tree he just had to scamper up the tree and take a hold of it. On one occasion, Orion was truly bewildered when he saw Lepus bolt past Procilina, who was carrying a basket full of crayfish, in his eagerness to climb up a tree and gnaw on a vine that looked very much like the ropes that were woven by the people. Not only did Lepus race up the tree, he went way out on a limb, leaning out as far as he could to grab the vine. Orion couldn't believe what happened next. Lepus lost his balance and plummeted thirty feet to the ground. Stunned by the impact, he lay motionless on his back for a moment, looking as if he were mesmerized by the vine dangling above him. Lepus did not lie there long because he was resilient enough to bounce back quickly. A mere life-threatening fall would not put an end to his bizarre behavior. He lifted himself to his feet, threw caution to the wind and made a mad dash up the tree; all because he had an inexplicable desire to sink his teeth into a rope-like vine.

Lepus had become so impulsive that Orion began to have second thoughts about trying to find another cache for a tasty meal. No amount of growling, persuasion, or convincing argument, could make his brother amend his destructive behavior. As soon as Lepus saw the rope he would set upon it greedily, gnawing on it so zealously that it would soon be in tatters at the bottom of the pit. He defeated their attempts to raise the food so many times that

Orion temporarily gave up on the idea of indulging in more sweet treats and turned instead to more practical food gathering missions.

Orion was very puzzled by the behavior of Lepus. He, himself, didn't feel an overwhelming impulse to eat the rope and he couldn't understand the inability of Lepus to leave the rope alone. Orion thought that the actions of Lepus were a sign of weakness. "Why can't you stop yourself?" was the question that Orion asked Lepus continuously. Eventually, after successive bungled attempts to get at the food, Lepus began to feel less urgency to approach and eat the rope. Was it possible that he had he learned that his impulsive actions were actually preventing him from getting the reward of something sweet? His frenzied rope chewing had not been met with success on many occasions, and as a result, the rope had become less appealing. The fire within him appeared to have been extinguished for now.

Orion did not forget about the deliciousness of the sweet water. He still thought about the taste of the maple syrup and knew that, if he so desired, he had the ability to get his paws on some more. After some time had passed and it seemed that Lepus had outgrown his bizarre behavior, Orion decided to use his knowledge of the Great Forest and his talent for getting across the river to find another hidden cache.

Once again Orion led his brother on an adventure into the Great Forest, but this time Lepus stood back as Orion used his dexterous fore paws to release the rope from a tangle of brush. Orion slowly drew the rope toward him and lifted a sweetened pouch of pemmican up through the ground. Orion took the pouch in his fore paws and turned it about. This was a type of food that he was unfamiliar with, but he could tell by the aroma that it must taste good. Besides, they both knew that it had been carefully prepared by the women, and so it was bound to be scrumptious. He un-wrapped a tube of preserved pemmican, and took a bite. "Hmmm, delicious," he mumbled as he savored a tasty mouthful. The eyes of Lepus were fixed on his brother as he continued to munch. He reached out his fore paw and Orion offered him a taste. In an instant Lepus was transformed back into his impulsive self. He jumped up excitedly and grabbed the rope's ragged end. The exquisite taste of the people's food coupled with the memory of successful attempts to reach the food in the past had triggered his reaction. His raccoon mind had recognized the connection between the rope and the reward of sweetened food and he once again became a captive to his own reflexive impulses.

Orion stood back and watched in amazement as the rings on Lepus' tail began to fade right before his eyes. Lepus grasped the rope and handled it with his fore paws as if he were washing a crayfish. He seemed to be acting automatically and was truly unable to stop himself. Looking at his brother's tail, Orion knew instinctively that the faded rings had an ominous significance. He felt an escalating sense of foreboding as he stared at Lepus, and he made up his mind to take his brother far away from the people's food before matters went from bad to worse. Hearing his father's voice in his ear, he acted quickly to lead Lepus far away from this area of the forest and back to the safety of their home across the river.

CHAPTER
Eight

SIRIUS TROUBLE

"You've been up to no good again, haven't you Lepus? I can see that the rings on your tail are faded. What have you gotten yourself into this time?" asked Sirius with a tilt of his head and a squint of his eye.

"Oh, nothing big brother. Go back to staring at ant hills or whatever it was that you've been wasting your time on today," replied Lepus with a smirk.

Sirius looked at his brother with exasperation. "And how have you been spending your time Lepus?" asked Sirius. "What ingenious ideas have you come up with today? Which way is north? Where do the crayfish hide? Which tree makes the best shelter? Come on Lepus, try to impress me with your expertise."

"Take a walk, Sirius. Don't bother me. Just because the rings on your tail are the darkest in the family, that doesn't give you the right to lecture me. Do me a favor, forget that I'm alive. Ya know Sirius, you've always got your nose into something no one in their right mind would care about. Come on, lighten up. Try having some fun for once. You could learn a thing or two from me about having a good time," replied Lepus.

Procyona heard her sons bickering and tried to intervene, but Lepus was irritated and continued to taunt his brother.

"Ma, do you know what Sirius was doing the other day? He was tagging along with a mother otter and her pups trying to learn how to swim like them. Doesn't he know that raccoons can't swim as good as otters no matter how hard they try? It was so funny watching him floundering around while mother otter swam circles around him. Ha, ha ha. Better yet, he saw a mud dauber wasp gathering mud off the river bank and he started up a conversation with her about what she was doing with all that sloppy mud. Ha, Ha, Ha, Sirius was having a conversation with a nasty looking wasp! Isn't that the dumbest thing you ever heard? And just to prove to you that your son Sirius belongs in a nest with a bunch of cuckoos, I want you to know that Sirius also loves to get close to lightning strikes, of all things. And he thinks that I'm the stupid one in this family? Only an idiot would go near a fire to see how it spreads. Now that's really smart! You're lucky that your precious son, the one that you think is so handsome, didn't come home one night with all of his fur singed off. Then again, come to think of it, maybe he'd look better that way. Ha, Ha, Ha. Oh, that is a good one. I can just picture Sirius as bald as a baby bird. Ha, Ha Ha."

Procyona wasn't amused. She had quite enough of her snickering offspring. She took a deep breath and said with a sigh, "Now Lepus, don't talk to your brother like that. It is not funny. Sirius is very inquisitive and studious. May I ask what's wrong with that? Listen to your mother Lepus. I'm sure that you could accomplish a lot, if you would just try to apply your mind. It wouldn't hurt you to follow your brother's example. You could learn something from him."

Lepus looked down at the ground and mumbled, "yea, sure ma, whatever".

Sign Tracker heard voices being raised and came over to see for himself what the problem could be between his sons. He knew that Sirius was probably not the one looking to cause a commotion.

He began to talk to Lepus about the faded rings on his tail and warned him once again not to go anywhere near the food of the people. Sign Tracker knew all too well that under the right conditions, the signs for the food would become captivating. He talked to Lepus for a long time, but it seemed like most of his advice went in one ear and out the other. Lepus had found a way to get enjoyment out of life and he wasn't open to hearing about the risks. Eating a little morsel of tasty food couldn't do much harm, anyway. "What's the big deal?" thought Lepus. "I'm not listening to any of their gibberish. How could anything that tastes so good, be bad for me? I know how to live. Why don't they just get off my back? It's very simple, I'm cool and they're not. End of discussion."

Lepus finally lost patience with everybody's meddling. He tried his best to brush off their comments about his tail. "I'm OK," said Lepus. "I've just been a little under the weather lately. It's not a big deal."

Sign Tracker knew that his wayward son wasn't listening with rapt attention, but what he didn't know was that Lepus was grumbling to himself like this:

"Why Would I Listen?"

"Why would I Listen?
I knew you were Wrong.
So What, if you'd Love Me,
All My Life Long."

"I heard you the first time,
But what does it matter?
I'm a Youth in my Prime,
So just Cut the Chatter."

And so it was that Lepus went on his merry way unfazed by the advice and concerns of the family who loved him.

CHAPTER
Nine

≫●≪

ALATRO

One day when Orion was getting ready to forage within the Great Forest, Lepus decided to tag along. He knew very little about food gathering because he preferred to let others do that for him. Today, however, weary of his idle meanderings, he decided to accompany his brother on a food gathering expedition. Acorns and seeds they found in abundance which Orion gave Lepus to carry. They roamed through the forest for quite a long time; Orion locating the food while his brother trailed behind him dragging the bundle. Lepus soon grew tired of his ever heavier burden and began to gripe to his brother, but Orion was not about to let him start slacking off. He kept on pushing him farther, thinking that he could gather extra food for the family with his brother along to help carry the load. Lepus grumbled incessantly under his breath that this would be the last time he went into the forest with his hard working brother.

It was not long before Lepus became exhausted. He was not accustomed to this type of work, and couldn't keep up with his brother, so he decided that it was about time for him to take a break. He conveniently slipped from view and stole off by himself, taking shelter beneath a dense bush that was growing next to a rocky ledge. He made himself comfortable and lay down on his back to rest, with his forepaws covering his eyes. Lepus dozed peacefully beneath the bush until a gust of wind awoke him from his slumber. He slowly stretched himself, yawned, and blinked his eyes. Looking up through the twigs, he caught sight of something above him reflecting color like a prism and wavering gently in the breeze. "Hmm, what could that be?" thought Lepus. It looked wide and yet almost invisible depending on the angle of the sun beams shining upon it. As it stirred gently in the air, he became more curious about what it was. It looked like a bunch of thin ropes woven together in a pattern of multiple strands. It reminded Lepus of the rope in the people's storage pit. Impulsively, he reached up to touch this strange looking object. It was rather tacky and stubbornly clung to him as he tried to shake it off his paw.

From deep within a rocky crag an eerie voice resonated in a menacing tone, "Who dares to disturb my creation!"

Lepus was startled and cried out fearfully, "It is I, Lepus, a simple raccoon. I mean no harm. It was an accident. I didn't mean to bump into your creation. Who are you?"

"Aye, a raccoon you say? How interesting," said the faceless voice. "I am Alatro and you have ruined my days work!"

Gradually emerging from the darkness of the stone crept Alatro. The sight of the creature which had spoken to him caused Lepus to catch his breath. Alatro was a hideous looking black widow spider. Though small, she was intimidating. A bright red hourglass on her abdomen showed distinctly against the background of her glossy black body. Her long spindly hind legs were covered with bristles, adding to the grotesque image. Lepus shuddered instinctively, his fur stood on end and his eyes bulged in fear. The black widow was within inches of him and her needle shaped fangs could inject her poison into his veins at any moment. Lepus became terrified as the black widow violently spewed her threats. "You owe me you stupid raccoon!" raged the spider. "You damaged my web, you idiot! Do you think that I'm going to let you get away with this? I should jump onto your face and plunge my fangs right into your nose, you clumsy fool. Don't even think about testing me because I'll make sure that you spend your last day in agony. Now, think carefully before you answer this question. Are you ready to make it up to me?"

Lepus was dumbfounded. He didn't know how to react. He started making promises that he couldn't keep and blurted out anything he could think of that would reduce the anger of the black widow. The spider, meanwhile, sized up Lepus as the perfect dupe for her diabolical plans. Lepus was ready to agree to do anything that the black widow proposed. The spider then changed her tune in order to make the most of this chance encounter. The deception had begun in earnest.

"Do not be afraid young raccoon," said the spider in a tone

meant to feign gentleness. "I will not harm you. I have a bad temper sometimes, that's all. I must have woken up on the wrong side of the web this morning. Calm down young raccoon. Let me introduce myself. My name is Alatro and I have been living here for a very long time. Don't worry about a thing. I have plenty of silk to rebuild my web. Listen, let's start over. Maybe we can be friends. Wouldn't you like that? I shouldn't have yelled at you. Come on, let me make it up to you."

Lepus stumbled backward and then started to inch away from Alatro. "Why are you shying away?" asked Alatro. "Come closer, I won't hurt you. I'm not nearly as bad as I look. Relax, take it easy. I've got something very special that will make you feel much better. I guarantee that a dose of my toxic blend - oops, I meant magic potion - will make all of your bad feelings wash away. It's absolutely mind-blowing and never disappoints. Trust me, it's to die for."

The spider quickly darted into a crevice and within seconds came back carrying a small thimble sized container suspended from woven strands of thread. She had fashioned a rope out of her sticky elastic capture threads and used drops of glue to attach it to the silken container. She dangled the prize before Lepus and told him that it contained a magical potion. Lepus was intrigued. He became excited at the prospect of trying something mysterious and forbidden. It took but a moment before he agreed to go along with any proposition that the black widow threw at him. He didn't know or couldn't imagine that the spider had created a drink made out of her poisonous venom. She now presented it to Lepus as a peace offering that she promised would make him feel absolutely fantastic.

Lepus was ill-suited to match wits with the treacherous Alatro. He was gullible, impulsive, and weak in spirit. More importantly, he thought of himself as quite the contrary. The false confidence that he had in his own imagined strengths led him to act without caution, and his weakness of character caused him to yield under pressure. The evil spider began to entangle Lepus in her silken web. She knew how vulnerable this naive raccoon would be to any manner of persuasion and that he could very easily be led astray. Alatro concluded that she would be handsomely rewarded for the time that she invested in him. What predator wouldn't pounce on such a prize? It would be child's play to manipulate this young raccoon.

Alatro simply appealed to Lepus's desire to experience something unusual that would make him feel brave and adventurous. But, unbeknownst to her, it would be even easier to "rope him in" than she expected. He had already developed an impulse to approach objects that resembled the rope that he and his brother had used to retrieve the people's delicious food. It did not take long before the young and foolish Lepus reached out to take the silken vial from the black widow's grasp. He then eagerly gulped down the spider's venom laden draught.

A transformation began to come over Lepus as a wave of euphoria washed over him. He had never felt such a pleasant rush of exhilaration. He felt invincible, but his breathing was labored and his heartbeat quickened. His senses began to alter. His perception of the world around him changed until the ordinary world didn't exist anymore. Somehow, this potion had made him feel powerful and gave him immense pleasure even though he could sense that his body was under a tremendous strain. He felt a tinge of nausea and then began to sweat profusely. His life force was being corrupted and his body responded by trying to rid itself of the venom. The intoxicated Lepus was completely oblivious to the ominous message implicit in these subtle cues. His senses were overwhelmed. As his eyelids grew heavy, a rush of luxurious pleasure surged from one end of his body to the other. Life ebbed and flowed through his veins as the skin beneath his black mask tingled and the muscles in his legs quivered. Lepus felt like he had entered another world and this feeling was so exciting that it overrode the ill effects of the potion. The black widow's venom was extremely potent. It changed his state of awareness and brought him to a place where he felt a sense of being outside of his body. Alatro's potion made him feel extraordinary and from the point of view of Lepus, this was a vast improvement over his usual state of mind.

The spider observed with delight the reaction of this hapless raccoon and with a sinister grin lighting up her hideous face, she advanced her scheme to further exploit her latest victim. "I will insist that this dullard bring me the sweet water being brewed by the people on the other side of the river. He'll gladly trade every drop that he can get his paws on for my alluring potion," thought

Alatro. "Soon enough, he'll be hooked on my venom. The rest is

easy. Once he feels the craving for another dose, he'll do whatever

I ask him to do."

The treacherous black widow intended to use the sweet water

near her web as bait. Insects attracted to the scent would stumble

into the sticky threads of her web. She would be feasting and

engorging herself indefinitely. "This is almost too easy," gloated

the spider. "This dim-witted raccoon will die a little every time he

drinks my potion and yet he will become more and more desirous

of it. It will be obvious that the venom is killing him, but he will be

so delirious that he won't care. Mark my words, when he gets that

ferocious craving for my potion, he'll do anything to get his paws

on some more. This stupid fool will race around in a frenzy

pleading for more of my potion, even though it's destroying him

from the inside out. I've seen this play out many times before. I

kind of get a charge out of kicking back and watching the action.

At first, when he reaches for the vial it will seem like there's

nothing to it, but then something mysterious will start to take over,

because he'll reach for the vial over and over and over again, like he's possessed. There's more going on here than meets the eye, that's for sure. He'll be touching the invisible ... touching something mysterious and powerful that no one can see, but somehow everyone can feel it and knows it's there."

Ha, ha, ha," the black widow laughed heartily. "I can see that this raccoon hasn't the least bit of savvy or self-control. And, what if he did? By the time he gets the first inkling of what's really happening to him, he'll be so far gone that there will be no hope of his escaping from my tangled web."

Alatro's eyes flashed as she recalled the slow deaths of her previous victims; those unfortunate creatures who had become entangled in her lethal, complex web. "I remember very well some of my prey who were strong and hearty struggling desperately to pull themselves away from my silken web. Tough luck for them; my web is inescapable. Sure, they make a valiant effort to break away from my durable strands, but it's useless to resist. The sticky threads hold fast while they spin and twist in vain. Then I move in for the kill, my fangs poised to deliver the final strike. No more struggling for them. My venom paralyzes their muscles swiftly, and before you know it, they are in excruciating pain and powerless to resist. Ah, the joy of watching their helplessness. In a flash, I wrap them up in my silken threads, and then it's time to settle down for my liquid lunch, hmm tasty."

The black widow polished her red hourglass as she hashed out her diabolical plans for the young raccoon. "I can just see it now," laughed the spider. "Lepus dragging himself over to my web, the rings on his tail gone, his eyelids swollen, bones sticking out of his fur, and all the while he'll be begging me for more of my venomous potion. Ha, ha, ha. I know a fool when I see one. He will bring me the sweet water, and lots of it. Yes, I know that I've gotten a bad reputation around here because of some of the things I've done, like eating my useless mates, but who cares? I'm invincible. I don't have to answer to any of these fools. I'll do whatever I want. This chump is exactly what I've been waiting for and he fell right into my web."

The spider had quite an uproarious laugh while Lepus sat back on his haunches bedazzled by his surroundings. With eyes aglow he stared blankly into the sky. His mind had left its earthly surroundings for now, but soon, the potion would begin to wear off. The spider was thrilled because as soon as Lepus came to his senses he started to tell the spider how eager he was to try out more of the potion. When she didn't give him another dose, he licked the inside of the silken container searching for any drops that were left. After twirling it around in his nimble forepaws he became assured that it was completely dry and pleaded with Alatro for another dose, but the spider had other plans. "Oh sure, I'll share my potion with you," said Alatro, "but it will cost you. It's very simple. If you want more of this potion, go across the river to the camp of the people and find out where they are brewing the sweet water. Bring a fresh cupful back here to me and I will share my magical potion with you."

For a moment Lepus considered the dangers of approaching the people's camp and stealing the sweet water, but he quickly brushed aside these concerns. Too young and naive to realize that the entanglements of the web could indeed prove fatal, he accepted the terms of the spider and looked forward to his upcoming adventures. He was young. How was he to know how fragile life could be? The black widow grinned smugly as she envisioned herself devouring an endless supply of tasty insects. Breathing a sigh of contentment, she rightly assumed that she already held sway over this simple-minded raccoon. It was only a matter of time before she was feasting on a bounty of plump beetles. "Hmm, Hmm," hummed the black widow to herself, "it is going to be so delectable to suck the life out of those juicy, sweet bugs."

A voice called from within the Great Forest. It was Orion searching for his brother. The spider warned Lepus not to divulge their plans and told him to keep Orion out of the picture so that her plot would not be in jeopardy. Lepus didn't particularly know how to make plans. He wasn't practiced in the art of designing tactics and so this was going to become very difficult for him. However, he was willing to take risks and struggle for what he wanted.

And so it was that Lepus became preoccupied with his quest to find the people's camp and in his raccoon mind his thoughts repeated incessantly, "Alatro's potion is so good. I can't wait to get my paws on the vial and down another dose of that potion. I wish that I was taking it right now. I have to get to the other side of the river. I must find a way to get to the sweet water."

CHAPTER
Ten

VANISHING TRUTH

The family of Sign Tracker lived well by the shores of the

Great Lake where they were never in want of food or shelter.

Many tall trees grew in the forest providing Sign Tracker's

family with hollows that made comfortable dens. Here they could

take refuge from the elements and sleep in peace. The family

especially loved to explore groves of the red maple tree where

they could easily find food and slumber for long periods of time.

When they weren't climbing trees they spent most of their time

wading in shallow water searching for tasty aquatic animals. Life

was going well for the family of Sign Tracker and he was

grateful for the many gifts that had come from the Great Forest.

Sign Tracker never ventured across the river, but on the days when the depth of the river fell and the force of the current subsided, he thought of the people living on the other side. He would sit on the river bank and gaze across the rippling water at the lush green plants growing on the other side. The smoothness on the surface of the river looked inviting and he was confident that he could make the swim to the opposite bank. It was then that he would reminisce about days gone by when he had shared a moment with his old friend Mapache. He missed the people, he missed Mapache, and he especially missed the people's food. However, he did not venture across. Experience and the ties that bind prevented him from reaching out to the people. Instead, he diverted his attention to other things and gave thanks that he and his family were safe on the south side of the river where they belonged.

Lepus, on the other hand, spent his days trying to come up with a way to get across the river safely. Unfortunately, without his brother to guide him, he could not find his way across the river or locate the people's camp. This presented him with quite a dilemma because telling his brother the truth was out of the question. Alatro had warned him not to let anyone in his family know about the deal they had made. Orion would never agree to help him cross the river if he were aware of his true intentions. Somehow he must fool his brother into helping him find the maple syrup without arousing the slightest suspicion that Alatro was involved in his plans. How was he going to talk Orion into helping him with his scheme?

Lepus recalled the feeling that he had gotten after using Alatro's potion and this gave him an incentive to push the limits with his brother. He knew that it was wrong to deceive him, but whenever he thought of the thrill of getting more of the magic potion he came up with excuses to justify his lack of decency. Lepus had reached the first major step of his downward spiral. He had started to lie to himself. He convinced himself that betraying the trust of everyone around him wasn't really so bad and that the consequences of becoming an elaborate liar were not that serious. He learned to reject the possibility that his lies, distortions and half-truths would eventually bring immense harm to his entire family.

Lepus would have to concoct a story that Orion would accept even though it was not even remotely true. He spun tall tales in his head trying to come up with a story that his brother would believe. None of his ideas seemed to make any sense. He would just have to hope that Orion would think that his explanation for wanting to cross the river was reasonable, even though it was groundless and based entirely on lies. He had to keep Orion completely in the dark by misleading him. Hopefully, if his lies were convincing enough, Orion would have no idea of the real purpose he had in mind.

Lepus did not foresee that he was about to become a most pitiful raccoon that no decent raccoon could ever trust or respect. He foolishly started down the path of deception without fully realizing the price he was about to pay. What would happen if his family caught on to him? How would they react? Disappointment, anger, frustration or worry, which would it be? Where was this path destined to lead him? He would have to adopt the character of a shameless raccoon who could pile one lie on top of another until his thoughts became so mired in a

quicksand of falsehoods that the truth completely vanished from

his thoughts.

"I got it!" thought Lepus, "I will tell Orion that I heard from

a very good source that a pocket bursting with salmon is waiting

on the north side of the river. I will convince him that this is the

biggest run of salmon ever seen and that it is there for the taking.

I'll have him believing that we will be able to bring back bushels

of fish for our family in no time. After all, it might be true.

Neither one of us has any way of knowing for sure what will

happen. Maybe we'll luck out. Orion has no real reason to

disbelieve what I say. How is he going to check up on me,

anyway? Orion expects me to be truthful and I can use that to my

advantage. Who knows? It might turn out that there is some truth

to my story. It's a possibility; we could catch lots of fish. He'll

be excited to try a new fishing spot if he thinks that we can catch

more fish on the north side of the river than we ever could've

caught over here. Knowing my brother, he'll be pleased by the

thought of how proud the family will be when we show up with a bushel of tasty salmon. Guaranteed, Orion will buy into the whopper I dreamed up hook, line and sinker."

Lepus now had a good reason to talk to his brother Orion, and together they roamed throughout the Great Forest. Orion was pleased to have Lepus along and liked showing him how much more familiar he had become with their territory. Orion could not quite understand his brothers new found enthusiasm for foraging, but he put aside his fleeting suspicions that Lepus must have an ulterior motive. What that motive was, he could never have imagined.

The day that Lepus had been longing for finally arrived. The river was at a low ebb and Orion decided that the circumstances were right to cross over to the other side of the river in search of the large hold of salmon that Lepus had promised. Orion searched and found the safest crossing point. The two brothers launched themselves out into the water, strongly swimming for the northern bank.

As soon as Lepus arrived on the opposite shore he became

anxious to find the people's maple syrup. He fed Orion an endless string of lies in order to induce him to go deeper into the forest toward the area where the people were brewing the sweet water. When Orion grew hesitant or contradicted his brother's senseless ideas, Lepus simply invented a new set of lies and pretended to be very confident that his statements, which were completely false, held some truth in them.

Eventually, the brothers came upon what Lepus had been searching for all along, a group of the people busily transforming the sap of the sugar maple tree into maple syrup and sugar. Lepus was intrigued. With Orion beside him, he quietly approached the women and children who stood amongst the pots of boiling syrup. Together the brothers climbed up a tree in order to get a better view of the action. From this vantage point they could see the simmering pots of maple syrup and clouds of steam rising above the bubbling brew. When the breeze shifted, the nose of Lepus came alive as he caught a whiff of the warm, sweet smell drifting upward in the cold air. "Ho!" he exclaimed as he leaned out to the end of a branch. "So this is how the fabled food of the people is made. No doubt it's delicious! Hmm, hmm, hmm, I'd love to dip my snout into that honey pot! Come on Orion; let's go get a taste of what they're brewing. I'm sure they won't even notice us."

Orion recalled very clearly the words of Sign-Tracker. Their father had warned them not to go anywhere near the food of the people. "Never," spoke Orion sharply. "Father warned us about the foods of the people. We were reckless, but now I've had a chance to think about it, and I'm not going after the people's food any more. We were really lucky that we didn't get hurt after we raided their food stores. Our Father said that not only will the people become angry at us for meddling with their food, but long ago before we were born, he tasted it and somehow it altered him in a terrible way. I never did quite understand the reason why he considered their food so deadly, but I know that the words of our father are true words. I don't care how appealing their food may seem, it is as our father has said, we must stay away from the food of the people."

Lepus was barely listening. What did his brother know about

the food of the people, anyway? He was determined to steal some of the sweet water and he really didn't care about how Orion felt about his bold plan. Nevertheless, Lepus needed to make sure that Orion didn't interfere with his scheme to bring some of the sweet water back to the black widow. He tried to convince Orion that tasting some of the syrup was just a harmless prank, but his brother wasn't buying it. Orion had already seen for himself that when the circumstances were right, Lepus would lose control of himself and become drawn to the people's food and all the things that were associated with it. When gentle persuasion failed to accomplish his purpose, Lepus became severe with his brother, accusing him of not having the backbone to take a sip of the sugary brew. He even scoffed at Orion and told him that he would probably end up just like their father, an old dud.

Orion grew angry at his brother's foolish remarks. He knew that the words of Lepus were far from the truth, but the fact that Lepus was making an attempt to goad him with hurtful words made him lose his temper. Besides, how dare Lepus speak in such a disrespectful manner about their father. Orion thought about grabbing Lepus by the snout and hurling him to the ground, but he stopped himself. "I would rather live as a dud than die as a fool, Lepus," shouted Orion in disgust.

Orion was angry and frustrated. He didn't realize it, but his loyalty to his brother was being challenged. He felt that it wasn't right to leave Lepus here to pursue his foolhardy scheme, and yet, he had been offended by Lepus and wanted him to learn a lesson the hard way. He knew that his brother was putting himself into a dangerous situation, but he was reluctant to step in because Lepus had just insulted him. Orion's thoughts crossed over themselves time and time again." Does he think that he can get away with talking to me like that?" Orion grumbled to himself. "What am I supposed to do? Should I go home and tell somebody what he's up to? Should I stay here and try to keep him out of trouble or should I go back home and let him do his own thing? Father is not going to like this one bit and Momma will be mad at me for leaving Lepus behind."

Orion started to move away, but he was very torn about what he should do. Was he doing the right thing? Something told him that he wasn't, but his brother's behavior made him angry and a bit irrational. After mulling it over for a few more minutes he slid down the tree and stomped away empty-handed. Orion felt totally disgusted with Lepus. He strode through the forest quickly as he muttered to himself about his brother's foolish ways:

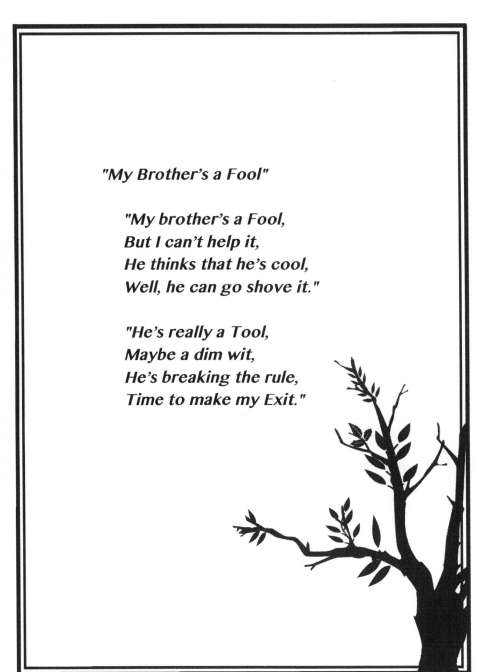

"My Brother's a Fool"

"My brother's a Fool,
But I can't help it,
He thinks that he's cool,
Well, he can go shove it."

"He's really a Tool,
Maybe a dim wit,
He's breaking the rule,
Time to make my Exit."

And so it was that Orion headed back towards the river, leaving his brother at the mercy of his own ruinous impulses.

CHAPTER
Eleven
—❖—

CLOSE CALL

Lepus circled the area where the kettles of maple syrup were boiling. He watched as a woman stirred the syrup with a ladle and then poured some into a clay pot by the kettle's side. After she sealed the pot and moved on, he crept up to where the clay pot lay and picked it up with his nimble fore paws. Gripping it tightly he scurried into the underbrush and lay low to conceal himself from anyone who might walk by unexpectedly. There was enough syrup dripping along the side of the pot to give Lepus a good amount to taste. Its sweet smell was tantalizing and he began to lick the pot gingerly. The sweet water spread over his tongue and down his throat. He paused for a moment to savor the sweetness of the syrup.

"Yummm," murmured Lepus to himself as he licked the pot clean. "Everything is going great so far. Now all I've got to do is figure out how to get this container of syrup back to the black widow. Things are really looking up for me lately. I made two fantastic discoveries. First, I found a cache of the people's delicious food and now I found out where they brew the sweet stuff. On top of that I met Alatro and discovered a magic potion that's out of this world. I finally broke away from the dull routine and caught on to something good. I'm really on a roll!" He moved his tongue busily, lapping up every drop of syrup. He liked the unusual taste and continued licking until he tasted nothing but clay. He then hid himself within the safety of the thick underbrush where he could watch and wait from close by.

In a short time a woman came back to check on the kettle. Taking some firewood from a pile close by she stoked the fire beneath the kettle until the fire was once again at its peak. Using a ladle that hung beside it she proceeded to stir up the boiling brew. Lepus waited for his chance, and as soon as she had replaced the ladle and was out of sight he quickly dashed out from his hiding place to where the ladle hung dripping with hot syrup. The ladle's thick coating of sticky syrup was enticing. He started to drool profusely. He picked up the ladle with his nimble fore paws, twirling it and licking it spotlessly clean. Dipping it back into the hot liquid, he scooped up a ladle full of sweet water and blew on it so that it would cool faster. He cautiously brought the hot syrup to his lips, sipping it slowly as steam wafted past his nose. When the syrup had cooled down to the point that it would no longer burn him, he gulped down a huge mouthful, and then continued to pour the remainder of the syrup down his throat.

Lepus needed to get a hold of himself. He was not one who believed in limitations and would have continued to engorge himself had he not been startled by the sound of the women approaching. He dropped the ladle abruptly and dashed off into the cover of the underbrush. There he hid licking the remainder of the syrup off of his sticky fore paws.

Lepus was frightened by the sound of footsteps and crouched low to the ground as more of the people walked near his hiding place. They had come very close to catching him in the act of stealing some of their syrup. It was a dangerous situation, but there was no doubt that Lepus fully intended to take the pot of syrup with him. Of course, if he carried the clay pot off, the people might miss it and catch on to his thievery. What would happen if they noticed that the pot was gone? Although he chose not to admit it to himself, he knew very well that the people had a reputation for certain vengeance. He knew that they would not like him sticking his nose into their kettles and might very well take drastic measures to keep his raccoon nose out of their sweet brew. These thoughts, although unsettling, were not enough to deter him. The hesitation brought on by his fears was no match for his primitive impulses and so he snuck out from underneath the bushes carrying the clay pot along with him.

"Who cares what my family thinks," thought Lepus. "This sweet stuff tastes great. Better yet, when the spider sees the pot of sweet syrup that I have brought for her she'll give me another dose of that magic potion of hers. There's nothing that my family has to offer that is as exciting as the potion in Alatro's vial. What do they know anyway? Their lives are so routine, so drab, so predictable. When are they going to shake it up a bit like I am? Especially Sirius, what a nerd he is! How can anyone waste so much time studying worthless things like ant hills, otters, night owls, wasps, and ridiculous stuff like that. Who cares? Oh, forget it. Why am I bothering to trouble myself with such drivel? So what if it's risky. I can handle it. I'll just keep my paws clamped on this pot of sweet stuff and get out of here. Pretty soon I'll be back at the black widow's web. Surely she will reward me with lots of her magic potion when she sees the pot of sweet water that I'm bringing for her. This is going to be fantastic! I better get moving before Orion comes looking for me. I just can't wait until I see the spider. She'll hook me up with a dose of that magical potion of hers. Gotta go, gotta go, gotta go!"

Lepus held tightly to the pot, trying to hold it level so that it wouldn't spill as he scurried away. Fortunately for him, the lid formed a tight seal and would not open easily. But, what he did not know was that the women had already noticed that something was amiss. Lepus had no idea that the people could easily detect his raccoon tracks leading right up to the boiling kettle. He also underestimated the amount of time and effort they had spent in order to boil down a small amount of syrup, and therefore, they would not tolerate his thievery.

Lepus hurried back toward the river carrying the clay pot tucked underneath his right foreleg. He couldn't remember what part of the river he and Orion had swum across. He rushed toward the river as fast as he could, but protecting the pot from harm slowed him down. When he reached the river he ran along the bank searching for a safe place to wade in. Rustling leaves, snapping twigs and moving branches gave away his position. The fact that he had stolen the syrup and was headed for the river was no secret. Mothers called out to their young sons to pursue him.

Lepus' search for a place to embark ended rather abruptly when a speeding arrow grazed the fur of his neck and drove into the ground just inches away from him. He took long strides then and leaped off the river bank and into the water. The powerful current pulled him downward. Refusing to let go of the clay pot, he fought to reach the surface of the water and swam furiously to get away from the deadly arrows. The young boys had been out practicing their hunting skills when they had been urged to give chase. They now launched their arrows into the air in quick succession hoping for a strike to his lungs. How proud they would be if they managed to end the life of this thieving raccoon. Lepus struggled to stay afloat not knowing which to fear more, the river or the missiles which were falling all around him. He floundered as he was tossed around by the current like a dead leaf. Still, he refused to let go of the pot of syrup. He clung to it desperately and swam for his life.

Lepus knew that the end could come at any moment, but as fate would have it, today was not the day for him to die. Tall trees leaned far out over the water, their roots giving way in the loose mud of the river bank. The water was full of snags, sand bars and driftwood. Lepus' journey down river was slowed by many obstacles. When a floating log passed near him he managed to grab a hold of it with his free foreleg. This piece of wood kept him above the water as he maneuvered through the debris clogging the river. With all the strength he could muster Lepus finally made it to the southern shore. Exhausted, he dragged himself through the mud and crawled his way up the side of a steep and slippery river bank. The water he had swallowed caused him to cough and wretch violently. With what strength he had left he rested the clay pot, full of Alatro's payment, upright on a piece of level ground. There he lay motionless with his fur covered in mud, not looking much like a raccoon at all, but blending in seamlessly with the debris that surrounded him.

Lepus rested for quite a while. After he caught his breath, he began to wipe the drying mud off of his masked face. He wiped his eyes and turned his thoughts away from his dangerous encounter with the people and began thinking about Alatro. He was determined to find her. Picking up his precious container of syrup he moved off in search of the black widow's web. He struggled to remember exactly where he had last seen her. The thought of the spider offering him a dose of her alluring potion quickened his heartbeat. "If only I had that vial in my paws right now," Lepus repeated to himself. He yearned to hold the vial up to his lips again.

Lepus trudged through the forest looking for signs that led to Alatro's lair. As he approached, he could feel the power of her mysterious potion drawing him closer and closer. The excitement was building. He couldn't wait to see Alatro in all her evil splendor reaching out her spindly black legs to dangle the vial in front of him. Lepus imagined her glossy black body marked with a red hourglass. Instinctively, he recognized this mark as a warning that she could be very dangerous, but sensible thoughts like this were fleeting, and didn't really matter. No amount of danger was a deterrent. He was unrelenting in his quest to meet her.

At last Lepus reached his destination and called out to the black widow excitedly. "Alatro, Alatro, it is I, the raccoon Lepus. I have brought you what you asked for. I have the sweet water. Come see. Here it is. Come see."

The black widow, who was suspended beneath her web, heard the voice of Lepus calling to her eagerly. "That was too easy," she chuckled to herself. "I didn't have to do a thing. All I had to do was give that dim-witted raccoon a dose of my venom, and now, it does the dirty work for me. He's dying to get more of my amazing potion. He'll do just about anything to get his paws on some more. I'll see him groveling like a slave soon enough. It's so entertaining to watch this jerk fall all over himself. If he had any sense at all he would have noticed by now that the rings on his tail are fading away. Oh well, I guess it's time to go see what that foolish raccoon has brought for me and it better be good."

At the sight of the black widow Lepus became impatient. A sense of urgency overwhelmed him. His breathing was shallow and rapid and his chest felt like it was clasped in a vice. He showed her the pot which was full of maple syrup. The black widow was pleased with Lepus and accepted the syrup as payment for a dose of her mysterious potion. First, she fashioned a container out of her strong silk and lined it with leaves, then she told Lepus to pour some of the syrup into her container. This would be used as bait to attract lots of juicy insects. She was confident that she would never run out of bait because she could always send Lepus back for more. That is, if the people didn't first hunt him down and finish him off, because he dared to sneak away with their sweet water.

Alatro told Lepus that he had done well. Then she crept deep into a crevice in the rock and came out with a vial full of her venom laced potion dangling from the twisted threads of her web. Lepus eagerly took it from her and began to drink it down. His expression changed as he savored the feeling that came over him when the venom began to course through his veins. His brain was flooded with Alatro's poison which set off a wave of hallucinations. He no longer cared where he was or what he was doing. He welcomed the obliteration of his mind and fell back on his haunches staring blankly into the distance.

It was the nature of Lepus to enjoy this escape from reality, but it would not last forever. Before long he began to come down from the venom- induced stupor. When this happened, he immediately felt the need for another vial of Alatro's evil brew. She offered him another dose, which Lepus consumed without hesitation. But, something was different. The venom didn't seem to have the same impact on him as it had the first time he had tried it. The effects were not quite as intense nor as pleasurable. Lepus may have been ignorant and gullible, but his body was not. His system had already adjusted to the poisonous venom. As Lepus developed tolerance he was going to need more and higher venom-laced doses in order to feel the effects of the potion. His body had become less responsive to its transforming effects. Nevertheless, he kept asking Alatro for more. The black widow refused, and in a crisp tone informed him that she would not give him another drop without payment. He would have to take an enormous risk and go back across the river to steal some more of the people's syrup. Lepus assured the black widow that she could count on him to do just that, and whatever else was necessary to bring back the syrup, as long as she agreed to give him a bigger dose of her magic potion the next time they met.

Lepus decided that he had better head back home for now. His family, especially Orion, would be looking for him. He slowly meandered through the Great Forest relishing his phenomenal experiences. All he could think about was getting more of Alatro's magical potion. Lepus understood that going back to the territory of the people was very risky. He knew that he needed a strategy that would allow him to once again steal some of the syrup away from the people. The risks were worth it. He would bring the syrup over to where the black widow waited beneath her web and then receive his mind-blowing reward. Lepus held that picture in his mind's eye; Alatro with her eight spindly legs and red hourglass dangling the vial of her exquisite brew right in front of his nose.

Lepus tried to clean himself up before he met his family, grooming his fur the best he could and touching up his tail. He arrived at the lake to find the rest of his family happily eating the fish, nuts, and insects that they had collected. Lepus sat down with them and ate a small portion of the food, although none of it appealed to him as much now that he had indulged in the magic potion of Alatro.

And so it was that Alatro grew fat from the body juices she drained from the insects attracted to the sweet water, while Lepus grew weaker and more desperate to satisfy his growing appetite for Alatro's potion. Lepus was driven by a force that he could not understand or control. He felt an urgent need to ingest greater quantities of the black widow's potion even as its capacity to create pleasure diminished. Such was the nature of the powerful and mysterious force within him, a force that made him desire more venom, enjoy the effects of it less, take greater risks in order to get it, while at the same time poisoning his body to the brink of death.

CHAPTER
Twelve

~~~~~~~~~~~~~~~

MAPLE SYRUP FESTIVAL

The sound carried for miles over stands of timber, wooded shoreline, marshy ponds, steep cliffs, and open fields. The low, rhythmic beat was recognized by all those who dwelled within the Great Forest, especially the raccoon, Sign Tracker. The sound caught his ear as he roamed along the rocky shore searching for fish. Although the sound was faint, Sign Tracker recognized it instantly. It was the drum, the heartbeat of the people. Sign Tracker paused to listen to the low, rhythmic beating of the drum. He felt nostalgic for the days when he had been on friendly terms with the people and they had shared some of their scrumptious edibles with him. Right now his old friends were gathered together to celebrate the abundance of creation and give thanks to the Great

Spirit for the continuation of their lives. They performed rituals, played games, and put on a feast with all the foods they had preserved and gathered. There was an abundance of wild foods mixed with the crops they had grown. Corn, beans, and pumpkin were the staple of their diet along with the fish and wild game that they had gleaned from the forest. Central to this festival was the maple syrup and sugar that they had preserved for the feast. The people sang and danced with joy, giving thanks to the Great Spirit for creating the sugar maple tree. They lifted their voices together and chanted, "Let us unite our minds and recognize that we are all connected in life."

In the wigwam of Mapache a group of the people was gathered in council to discuss the status of their food supply. They knew that they had to preserve as many staples as possible in the abundant seasons of the year in order to ensure that an ample amount of food would be available to sustain all of the people during the lean months. Famine was not likely if they stored their food wisely. Although Mother Earth had provided well for the people, there were times of drought, fierce storms, and other bouts of ill fortune which had taught the people of their need to acquire skills that would help them to harvest food and preserve it. In their culture there was no such thing as one group eating freely while their neighbors went hungry. All sustenance was shared by those who had been successful in the hunt. A pot of stew simmered in every wigwam at all hours of the day and night and was available to anyone who was hungry. Those who suffered hardship were helped by their tribe and none were abandoned to starvation. These resourceful survivors considered any intrusion into their stores of food as a threat to their lives and would go to any lengths to prevent it. All were aware that raccoons had been getting into their food supply and all agreed that the sooner they rid themselves of this problem the better.

"We should place a dead fall trap near to the brewing sap," spoke the first warrior. "It is very simple. We will set it up so that when he approaches the kettles a great log will fall upon him and kill him instantly. This will put an end to this bothersome raccoon's life and any others who dare to come within sight of our camp."

Many believed that this should be done. The raccoon had gotten away with stealing their syrup before, but if the deadfall trap was set up skillfully it would make short work of this threat to their sweet ingredient. They planned to build several of these deadly traps immediately and set them around the camp and in the vicinity of the simmering kettles.

Mapache listened to the discussion with interest. From what the women described, he suspected that something was terribly wrong in the world of the raccoon. The tracks left by one particularly unusual raccoon told a story about how he was behaving. The raccoon did not show the degree of caution inherent in a raccoon's nature. His approach was forceful and hurried, his actions were reckless. He seemed to be unaware of himself or the risk he was taking. Mapache was certain that there was a hidden motive within this raccoon that could explain why his behavior had become so bizarre. He understood the habits of raccoons and this knowledge led him to conclude that there was a harmful force lurking amongst the raccoon nation. If the raccoon had been exposed to disease, all of the inhabitants of the Great Forest could be in serious danger. Was it a harmful disease that had made the raccoon lose control of himself and act as if a part of him had been corrupted? What powerful force had infected the raccoon that compelled him to behave so unlike a healthy animal? Didn't he realize the danger he was in? If the raccoons had been harmed by this mysterious force, would the people be next? These thoughts troubled Mapache and left him with a feeling of trepidation.

Mapache wanted to learn more about the raccoons and he spoke out in favor of trying to capture one alive so that he could examine the animal to see if it had been infected with a disease or injured in an unusual way. Unfortunately, under the circumstances, it would be very difficult to reason with the young warriors and dissuade them from carrying out their plan to put an end to this interloper. Not many would agree that the raccoon should be spared.

As the people discussed how to solve the problem, Mapache continued to ponder what the women were telling him about the strange behavior of the raccoons. He could easily understand why a cache of food would be devoured by them, but why would the rope that was used to raise the pots be so frayed? Mapache ran his hands over the rope that the women had brought to show him. It was clear that the rope had been chewed up by the raccoon and it was likely that he had swallowed pieces of it. Mapache was determined to get to the root of the problem. He remembered the incident that had occurred when Sign Tracker had been given food as a reward for delivering firewood, but this seemed much more serious than that. As these thoughts twined through his mind, he was filled with an uncanny sense that Sign Tracker was nearby and would be entering his wigwam again soon.

The hunters were eventually persuaded that there might be a good reason to capture a live raccoon. They agreed to let Mapache build his own traps which would be designed to capture the thief without harming him, but some still proclaimed that the raccoon was such a threat to their lives that the deadly traps also had their place. The people would leave it to chance. Should the raccoon wander into a deadfall trap, his life would be ended. But if he was caught in Mapache's trap his life might be spared. One way or the other the raccoon would no longer be free to invade their food stores.

As Mapache began to describe the trap that he would design to catch the maple syrup thief, in burst Rukeewis, a man who had once faced banishment from the tribe. He bellowed loudly, insisting that the young men were fools to listen to anything that

Mapache was saying. He hurled insults at Mapache, and ridiculed him for his blindness. The others in the room were astonished by this outburst. Everyone knew that Mapache was one of the most respected men in the tribe. He was renowned for the sacrifices he had made for his people and bore the scars of many battles to prove it. The children loved to go to the wigwam of Mapache and listen to him reminisce about the great deeds of their forefathers. He was by far the favorite storyteller among the children, weaving dramatic yarns that revealed the secrets of the world. The head chiefs of the tribe and young warriors regarded him as a wise and dignified leader. They turned to him in troubled times for sound advice and good counsel.

Rukeewis continued to rant as Mapache sat still as a stone, "He is a friend of raccoons. He will lead us all into famine. Maybe in the past he was a good hunter, but now look at him. He can't even see. Why would you listen to a blind man? The children should follow me. They shouldn't look up to a man who doesn't bring venison to the cooking fires. If he can't hunt and he can't go to war, what kind of a man is he? He belongs with the old women."

With that, Mapache abruptly turned his attention to the entrance of the wigwam. He heard the unmistakable sound of a man approaching with a quick, firm step. Gliding into the wigwam like a bird of prey swept Four Bears, the most esteemed man in the tribe. The enemy feared him, but the women adored him, because he was both noble and dangerous. Four Bears had heard the raised voice of Rukeewis and it had sent him into a rage. Not being a man known for restraint, he was eager to unleash a cruel punishment on the offender. Things were not going to go well for Rukeewis now. His bravado quickly faded into a quivering submissiveness. He froze, wide eyed and terrified as Four Bears bore down on him with his knife drawn. Before Rukeewis could escape his wrath, Four Bears seized him by the throat, tightening his grip like an eagle clasping his talons. Rukeewis did not dare to move or resist as Four Bears threatened to tear his scalp off.

Four Bears well remembered the day that the village was attacked by the enemy in great numbers. Mapache and Four Bears were young men at the time. The fighting was fierce as the women and children fled screaming from the enemy, who charged in to kidnap or kill them. Vastly outnumbered, Rukeewis ran from the fray, but Four Bears stood his ground. As the fighting grew desperate, Four Bears proved himself to be one of the most courageous warriors of the tribe. With deadly accuracy he let loose his arrows, killing three of the enemy. He continued to fight despite the continuous assault that left him bleeding from many wounds. This was the day that he earned his name, as the enemy later declared "he rushed on like four bears". As the fighting raged Mapache saw one of the enemy poised to deliver a lethal blow to Four Bears who had fallen backwards. Bleeding from deep wounds himself, and in the midst of the chaos, Mapache saved the life of his friend by hurling a lance at Four Bears' attacker, striking him through the neck. Four Bears regained his footing and fought valiantly with his double-edged knife, but Mapache collapsed when he was struck in the back of the head with a war club.

Mapache lay lifeless and was left for dead until the fighting subsided. It was dusk before Isquasis, the medicine woman, discovered his battered body. She carried him into her wigwam and treated his wounds with the help of another sage healer. For many days he lay in the hands of the Great Spirit, as Isquasis used a hollow reed to drip a healing tea over his lips. Fortunately for

Mapache, his body was young and strong. The healing skills of Isquasis and the mercy of the Great Spirit worked miracles on his injured skull. He eventually regained his strength, but he would never see another sunrise. Stalwart and humbled, he accepted his fate. He now lived an awakened life. A life of wisdom and enlightenment brought forth from his soul by his encounter with death.

Rukeewis later claimed to have been heroic during the battle. He joined the war dance and bragged that he had killed one of the enemy. It was Mapache who denied him and proclaimed to the tribe that Rukeewis carried the war shield of the coward. He stood up in council holding the sacred wampum beads and declared that Rukeewis' claims about his fighting skills were all lies. He urged the people to banish Rukeewis from the tribe because he had seen him running past the women in his eagerness to escape the fight. Rukeewis said that he could prove his bravery because he had taken a knife from an enemy that he had slain. He attempted to convince everyone that he was seen running past the women because he had gone to retrieve his weapons. However, no one came forward to say that they had seen Rukeewis fight during any part of the battle. Mapache was incensed that there were some lesser men of the tribe who defended Rukeewis and spoke as if they believed his ridiculous tale. Did they really believe his incredible stories? Why did the others not see him for what he was? Did they have some reason to protect him?

Mapache and Four Bears were convinced that nothing that Rukeewis said was true. They had an undisguised hatred for this coward and shunned him completely. They were outraged that Rukeewis managed to avoid banishment by winning the help of men who, like him, were not known for their skills, their bravery or their honor. With the aid of these miscreants, he escaped banishment and continued to spread his resentment and hatred of Mapache throughout the village.

Mapache shouted to Four Bears to put away his knife. It would be bad medicine to have the blood of this coward staining his threshold. Four Bears looked to his friend and then loosened his grip reluctantly. He wanted to strangle the life out of this despicable coyote whose insults were an offense to all men of honor. This was a society with no laws, other than a man's own virtue, and Mapache was arguably the most virtuous man of the tribe. Four Bears was not about to let this coward go before instilling within him the dread of knowing that this offense would not go unavenged. He promised Rukeewis that he would meet him again soon when there was no one to defend him. With this he loosened his grip and put away his knife. As soon as Four Bears let go of him, Rukeewis slunk out of the wigwam and lost himself among the revelers at the festival.

The people continued to enjoy their feast long into the night. Empty stomachs would never do at this celebration. The food was delicious and added to the joy of dancing and singing. Each member of the tribe sent up a prayer giving thanks to the Great Spirit for the abundance in their lives. The drums continued to beat an ancient rhythm that carried for miles into the dark corners of the Great Forest. It was a joyous time for the people, when each of them prayed for peace and raised their voices in a song of thanksgiving.

CHAPTER
Thirteen

NOTTURNO

"We all know that you're lying Lepus, so why don't you just come clean?" said Sirius to his brother with an exasperated tone.

"Yea, Lepus, no one believes anything you say anymore. None of it adds up. Do you really expect us to listen to a word that you say? Come on, you've been stealing the people's food haven't you? When are you going to stop stringing together, one ridiculous story after another. Give it up Lepus, you're not even a good liar," scolded Orion.

"Momma is so worried about you," said Sirius. "I saw her the other day out in the woods by herself. She was leaning over a fallen log with her head bowed. It was clear that a heavy burden was weighing her down and that she wanted to have some time alone, so I didn't make myself known. I held myself back as her tears fell softly to the ground. She began to tremble as her gentle teardrops swelled into a torrential downpour. I stood there helplessly; unable to move, unable to comfort her, believing that you, Lepus, were the cause of her sorrows. We all know that she cries because she is so disappointed in you Lepus. She wants to help you. Even though you've hurt her, she can't stop caring about you. She and father want to get you back on the good road. If only you would let them."

Lepus didn't let on, but he thought that he knew which day Sirius was talking about. It was the time that he had promised his mother that he would meet her over by the hardwood forest to help her gather chestnuts. As usual, Lepus had other thoughts on his mind, including taking a little detour. He came up with a sob story about how he had to leave for a minute to go check on a sick friend. Before Procyona could react, he abruptly took off, but swore that he would be right back to help her with the harvest. Procyona had no clue that what he really intended to do was meet up with some of his low-life friends for a quick fix.

Lepus soon proved how helpless he was in the face of temptation. At first he took just a swig of the potion and began to mellow out, but his degenerate friends kept waving vials of the potion in front of his face and urging him to do another shot. Lepus couldn't resist. He told his friends that he had to leave, but it was too late. Before long he had surrendered entirely to a mysterious force that made the vial irresistible. His blood was flowing with poisons and he reflexively brought to his lips any and all foul concoctions that came his way. Bleary-eyed, and lost in a hazy stupor, he stumbled out onto a trail and fell into a bog. There amidst the slime and muddy ooze, he passed out cold, but fortunately for Lepus he landed with his face above the water or surely he would have drowned. The next day when he came to his senses, he didn't even know where he was or how he had gotten there. Dragging himself out of the mud, he limped his way toward home, looking as if he'd been mauled by a bear. Along the way he made up lame excuses for himself to explain why he had messed up, yet again. Lepus really hadn't intended to ditch his mother. He foolishly believed that he could stop by his friend's place for a minute, indulge a bit, and move on. Unfortunately for Lepus, the reality was that he was compelled by symbols and driven by uncontrollable impulses. What had started out simple enough had ended up propelling him to the brink of death. Procyona was worried sick over her son and ever since that awful day she had been burdened with fear, disappointment, and heartache.

"Come on Lepus, tell us the truth for once. If you tell us the truth we can help you. Without knowing the truth we can't get you out of whatever mess you've gotten yourself into," said Orion.

"There's nothing to tell," said Lepus. "Sure, I've gotten into the people's food and had a few close calls, but I don't do that anymore. It's not my fault that Mom is so dramatic. How many times do I have to say it? I don't need help from anybody. Why don't the two of you just back off!"

The family of Lepus had become alarmed because of his bedraggled appearance and erratic behavior. It was clear that his body was weakening. He looked terrible. His fur was dull and discolored, his eyes looked past you, his teeth were rotting, he was always sleeping, and the rings on his tail were barely visible. Even the mask on his face had changed. It looked like the mask of a raccoon suffering from rabies.

The family rarely saw Lepus. He was always sneaking off by himself at night without telling anyone where he was going. He would be gone for days, even weeks, while his parents grew sick with worry. Without a word from him, they didn't know if he was dead or alive. When he came home from his rambling he would collapse into a deep sleep. Always very evasive, he wouldn't speak to his father and shied away from his sister's kind attentions. As for his mother, she longed to know what was happening to her son so that she could try to set him straight. Procyona wanted to nurture him back to health but it was to no avail. Lepus wanted nothing to do with her. The bond between them had been broken. It was like her son wasn't even her son anymore, and all she could do was watch him drift farther and farther away.

Sirius was not about to sit back and do nothing, especially after seeing his mother brimming with sorrow. He decided to take matters into his own hands. He and Orion had tried to track Lepus through the forest at night in order to discover where he was going, but their efforts had been futile. The darkness made it easy for Lepus to lose them. Sirius knew that he needed to ask for help. He set off in search of the one and only Master of the Night Skies - Notturno - the Great Horned Owl. Sirius was certain that Lepus would never be able to evade the watchful eye of the night eagle. Notturno could not be deceived. He would find out exactly what Lepus was up to. Lepus' days of deceiving his family would be over if owl agreed to do him this favor.

Sirius set off at dusk, just as darkness was beginning to enshroud the Great Forest. He had spoken to the owl once before, after bumping into him in the treetops one night long ago. At the time, Notturno didn't seem very interested in talking to him, but had been patient and tolerant of his presence. A loner at heart, the owl had looked him over, bobbed his head from time to time, and spoke only a few words. Nevertheless, Sirius was determined to search for the Great Horned Owl. If he approached him in friendship and with the utmost respect, the owl just might agree to help his family. He would never know unless he asked. Sirius would try to make his case persuasively and hope for the best.

Sirius walked quietly through the Great Forest heading for the place where he had last seen Notturno. He was anxious to find him and tilted his furry ears this way and that hoping to pick up the sound of the owl's unmistakable call. Sirius had to admit that he was very intimidated by the owl. Notturno was a fearsome hunter who glided through the Great Forest on silent wings. Seemingly out of nowhere, he would swoop down upon prey three times his size. Notturno's talons were as sharp as daggers and all who felt their grip died instantly. His large eyes shone golden yellow like no others. Every inhabitant of the Great Forest feared him, including the people, who were not willing to challenge him. His ominous call echoed through the darkness of the Great Forest putting fear into the hearts of all who imagined death, perched quietly overhead, waiting for the moment to strike. Notturno reigned over the Great Forest with stealth and power, visiting a certain death upon his unsuspecting prey.

After several nights of hoping that Notturno would appear, at last Sirius heard the owl's distinctive call, "hoo, hoo, hoooo, hoo, hoo." Sirius seized his chance. He called out to the owl in his own language and the owl responded. He scrambled up the tree that the owl was perched in and kept on calling out to him. When he reached the height of Notturno, he introduced himself politely and essentially begged him for help. He told him about his brother, the family's efforts to reach him, their mother's sorrow, and how grateful they would be if he would do them this favor. Sirius asked Notturno to discover where Lepus was disappearing to at night and with whom. He assured the owl that he was absolutely certain that no other animal living in all of the Great Forest was more suited to this task than him.

Notturno seemed to take a sympathetic view of Sirius. Being of noble character, he was impressed by the devotion of Sirius to his family. He knew that Sirius had come to him for unselfish reasons and that his request was reasonable. The owl agreed to track down his brother on one condition, that Sirius vow to honor the truth and take righteous action no matter what that would entail. Sirius did not hesitate. He was loyal and courageous. He would do what he must to satisfy his end of the agreement.

Owl told him to meet him at the same place in two weeks. He would do his best to answer all of his unanswered questions. He promised Sirius that he would begin observing Lepus immediately. Sirius thanked him profusely and reveled in delight at hearing owl's encouraging words. He scrambled back down the tree to share the good news with his brother Orion.

And so it was that Notturno became an ally of Sign Tracker's family. He began to observe Lepus intently from an oak tree overlooking the family's territory. The owl occasionally fluffed his brown feathers and stretched his wings, patiently waiting for Lepus to make his move. Other than the necessary hunting foray, Notturno kept a close watch over the whole family. Each of them went about the business of living, except for Lepus, who neither groomed himself nor searched for food. He seemed preoccupied with thoughts of far away places, sitting off by himself even when his kind-hearted sister called out to him.

The moment that Noturrno had been waiting for came as expected when his sensitive eyes caught sight of Lepus skulking off alone into the darkness of the Great Forest. The magnificent owl lifted off on his silent wings, easily gliding close to Lepus, unseen and unheard. To keep up with Lepus was not a challenge for this superior hunter, especially given the light of the moon. Notturno followed Lepus for quite some time, astonished to see him throw caution to the wind and boldly tramp across the forest floor. "Too bad his brains don't match his boldness," thought Notturno to himself.

On his broad wings the owl hovered above the forest floor, staying close by the side of Lepus until they arrived at a somber place hidden deep within the Great Forest. This seemed to be the end of the road for Lepus, and so Notturno settled down in a prime location, perched high in a tall spruce tree. Aloft and shielded from the eyes and noses of other animals, he kept watch over the scene below him. Notturno's roost gave him a clear view of the comings and goings of beasts of all kinds and he saw many of them approach what looked like an abandoned badger's den. Lepus greeted a few unsavory characters and then quickly crawled underground. He was followed by others who appeared to be familiar with this meeting place. What went on within the den was not apparent to the owl, but he was certain that many creatures were being drawn underground by something powerful that lurked within.

There was one particular animal that caught Notturno's attention far more than any of the others. It was an elegant female, the most beautiful red fox that he had ever seen. The owl's golden eyes remained fixed on her as she gracefully moved through the forest on her way toward the underground den. To this venerable owl she was an absolutely gorgeous vixen. The rich burnished red of her fur shone with the reflection of the moonlight. The warmth of the lustrous colors reminded Notturno of the western sky at sunset. The tip of her bushy tail, which was a luminous white, made it easy to track her movements as she slid through the undergrowth. Owl gazed at her in fascination. Her alluring beauty was a pleasure to behold. He kept her in sight as she paused for a brief moment on a low hill and then vaulted to the top of an upright stone. Notturno did not stir. He settled down in awed silence, marveling at the beauty of her silhouette against the starry sky. Her profile was so lovely and her pose so majestic that had she not jumped down from the stone, he could have remained enraptured by the view indefinitely. Notturno held himself steady upon his perch. He felt that he was in the presence of one of the most exquisite beauties ever fashioned by mother nature.

Waddling along behind the red fox was a bristly porcupine.
Notturno was taken aback to see this beautiful vixen consorting
with a scurrilous looking porcupine instead of another red fox.
Why had she left her own kind to be with this suspicious looking
character? Why wasn't she roaming about with a proper mate? She
entered the den after her companion, who beckoned to her
forcefully and led the way down into the underground passageway.
The last glimpse that the owl had of this striking female was the tip
of her tail being swallowed up by the darkness beneath the earth.

Notturno kept a vigil, camouflaged perfectly as he roosted on
a sturdy branch. He turned his neck from side to side keeping
watch over all that passed below him. Although the vixen had
entered the den after Lepus, she started to leave the den before
him. A rattlesnake slithered out from beneath her feet, and after
him came the vixen, stumbling awkwardly as she tried to make her
way out of the den. Notturno was stunned by the radical change in
her appearance. Her fur was covered in filth and mud. It looked
like she had vomited all over herself. She wobbled around on her
quivering legs which looked like they were about to give out.
Gradually she staggered away from the entrance, but it seemed as

if she didn't really know which way to go. She rocked to and fro, backward and forward until eventually she managed to start up the trail leading away from the den. Her progress was halting and slow. She stepped forward, lifting one frail paw after the other, trying to maintain her balance with every step. The owl was alarmed by what he saw next. With wide eyes he watched her collapse in a heap and pass out cold in the middle of the trail. Her tongue lolled out of her mouth and vomit spilled from her throat. It was an absolutely revolting sight. Owl observed all of this silently from his lofty perch. What had happened to this beautiful fox in the underground den? What had turned her into this wretched looking creature? Was she going to die right there before his eyes? Notturno could not hide his shocked disbelief. His dignified nature was offended by this pathetic sight. He needed to compose himself. A chivalrous instinct compelled him to protect her, but he believed that he could do nothing to save the red fox judging from her condition. The life of this vixen was in the hands of the creator. Only the one who gave her life could save it now.

It was clear to Notturno that the forces of evil lurked underground. A wide variety of species entered and exited this den of horror and none were the same when they left. The porcupine came out of the den not long after the vixen had passed out. Notturno hoped that the porcupine would help her because he noticed that this odd looking rodent paused to look at her on his way up the trail. But this was not what happened. The porcupine looked down at her nonchalantly, shrugged his nasty looking quills and nudged her with his spiny fore paw. When she didn't respond, he carelessly stepped over her, leaving the weakened vixen to fend for herself.

Noturrno had witnessed many a frightening and tragic event within the Great Forest, but the suffering of this beautiful vixen affected him like no other. He had watched with rapt attention as this enchanting red fox entered the underground den, only to be felled by an outpouring of grief when she reappeared cloaked in a shroud woven of death. Innocence and loveliness were gone, abruptly stolen away and replaced by a gruesome aura of horrific suffering. The noble owl felt a wave of foreboding wash over him. An ill wind blew across his downy feathers, sending a shiver to the tips of his rounded wings. Deep within his breast, a mournful call began to rise and move into his throat. Although his soul strove to resist, Noturrno could not escape the reality that what is pure and beautiful can be destroyed in an instant by fearsome cruelty. From his lofty perch he had watched in stunned silence as this vision of untarnished beauty was cast down and trampled into an ugly pulp.

Notturno remained aloft, continuing to observe the scene below him with intense interest. Lepus stayed within the den for days. What was he living on? As far as the owl knew there was no food being brought into the den. He heard little sound other than an occasional moan or murmur, a pleading whine, or a slurred word. Notturno remained on guard outside the den hoping for a glimpse of Lepus. His patience was rewarded when Lepus came forth from the den on the third day. Owl now fully realized why the family was so worried about Lepus and begging him for help. Lepus looked like a skeleton. It was amazing from the looks of him that he was still alive.

Owl continued to track Lepus as he had promised. The incident at the den was only the beginning of Lepus' misadventures. Just wait until the family of Sirius learned that Lepus had stolen a birch bark canoe and had used it to cross the river in order to cause mischief over at the people's camp. If that weren't bad enough, he had outdone himself by climbing up on the palisades surrounding the camp and then leaping onto the roof of their ceremonial long house. Once he got his bearings, he snuck into the long house through one of the smoke holes left open on the matted roof. He stayed inside but a short time and then came out carrying a rawhide bundle. Owl knew what this was. It was a block of sugar that the people had made to flavor their food. Was this what Lepus was willing to risk his life for? Why was this raccoon acting so jittery and reckless? Notturno continued to study this peculiar behavior. He was curious to see what dare-devil antics Lepus would come up with next. After his perilous escapade, Lepus hurried back to where he had hidden the canoe and paddled away as quickly as he could before the people awoke and discovered his thievery. Once back on the south side of the river, he didn't take any time to rest or to eat, instead, he hastily made a beeline for the mysterious underground den.

Notturno had seen enough. He would wait until the time was right and then he would tell Sirius exactly what he had learned about the actions of Lepus. The owl was a fiercely protective parent himself and felt a generous amount of compassion for the family. How had Lepus escaped the wrath of the people? How had he avoided smashing the canoe to bits on the rocks submerged in the rushing river? How had he stayed in the den without food for so long? Maybe he had been lucky so far, but eventually he would run out of chances. There was no doubt that this raccoon was doomed if his family didn't step in and pull him away from the evil that lurked in the forest. His days were numbered. It was only a matter of time.

CHAPTER

Fourteen

⟞⟐⟝

THE GREAT FALLS

The roar of rushing water made it impossible for Procilina to talk to her brothers. She needed to get their attention, but that wasn't going to happen until they had moved away from the white water pouring over the rapids. Procilina and her brothers had been foraging along the river, following the current downstream toward the coast. The siblings ventured beyond their home territory until they came to a gorge where the water became too rough to risk standing along the river bank. The rapids were not something to toy with and they knew that they needed to stay off the slippery rocks and tangled branches lining the river bank. They had heard stories about others who had been caught in the swirling current, swiftly carried over the edge of the falls and flung onto the huge boulders at its base.

Sirius, Orion and Procilina had traveled quite a long distance. They were ready to find a shelter in which to rest, but this thought vanished from their minds as soon as they caught a glimpse of the Great Falls. The stunning view stopped them in their tracks. Together they sought a good vantage point and made their way to a rock ledge overlooking this awesome wall of water. White foam and spray enshrouded them in the misty air, soaking their fur. It was a bit frightening to stand so close to the roar of nature's power. They stood squarely on their four paws but soon retreated to a much safer distance away from the ledge. This was a waterfall which dwarfed all others. Although the Great Forest was threaded with many rivers and falls, none approached the width of this one. Here was the greatest waterfall in the raccoon's world and they did not for a moment underestimate its immense power.

Procilina took her eyes away from the falls for a moment and noticed a bird gliding among the trees out of the corner of her eye. She nudged Orion and pointed up in the direction of the treetops behind them. Orion looked over his shoulder and saw the owl circling in their direction. He motioned to Sirius and they all moved deeper into the tree line. The owl called out a greeting as he alighted in the boughs of a white pine tree. He wasted no time with casual chatter and immediately began to inform them of their brother's escapades. The three siblings listened with rapt attention, the expression on their masked faces moving from furrowed brow, to wide-eyed bewilderment. Notturno told them a great deal of what he had observed, but even he, with his unparalleled powers of observation, did not know that the venom of Alatro was the poison that had turned Lepus into a member of the underground.

Sirius questioned Notturno in detail. He needed to know exactly where they could find Lepus and what conditions to expect when they met up with him. Notturno elaborated on what he had already told them and promised to guide them in the right direction. They all agreed to meet later on that night. They would seek out Lepus right before dawn because the owl was convinced that this would be the time when Lepus would be winding down from his ventures of the previous night.

Notturno left the siblings standing together conversing in rapid tongues. They did not know exactly what situation would confront them, but they knew that they had to find their brother and pull him away from the place where he was now. The three sat down in a circle discussing everything that Notturno had revealed to them. How were they going to persuade Lepus to come home with them and leave behind this dangerous lair in the dark recesses of the Great Forest? They did not know what state of mind he was in, but they resolved to track down their brother and drag him away from the place that the owl had described. How they would accomplish this feat they did not know, but they were intent on reaching Lepus before the sun rose on a new day.

CHAPTER

Fifteen

REFLECTION

At the edge of a forest clearing, where the deep woods open up to a grassy field, two brothers and their sister waited patiently for the return of Notturno. The moonlight provided some comfort in the predawn hours as Sirius, Orion, and Procilina sat together on top of a fallen log. Branches stirred above their heads and leaves rustled around them, but they were not listening to the sounds emanating from the darkness. Instead, they tilted their faces toward the sky hoping for a sign of Notturno's impending approach. He did not disappoint them. At the agreed upon time he emerged out of the darkness and landed on a branch above their heads. The Great Horned Owl was nearly invisible as he sat in a tree enshrouded by shadows. He repositioned his feet, fluffed up his feathers and settled himself down comfortably. The raccoons below him huddled closely together as the owl's huge pair of glowing yellow eyes stared down at them. Notturno agreed to lead them to the area where he had last seen Lepus, but he told them that at daybreak he would depart, leaving them to deal with their brother as well as they could. The raccoons understood that there was no time to waste because the owl would leave them when the sun began to rise. They hopped off the log and hurriedly followed Notturno as he moved through the forest, hovering low to the forest floor. As the raccoons scuttled after Notturno, the terrain began to change. The hills became harder to climb because they were littered with dead growth. The siblings trudged ahead with Notturno's encouragement and soon they arrived at a desolate looking area surrounding a stagnant pond. The water was quite still, as there was very little life surviving within its murky depths. The smells were repulsive to the young raccoons. It was here, in this somber place, that they came upon their vagabond brother.

"Would you look at him?" exclaimed Orion. "He's groping

around in the muck trying to catch bullfrogs! Gross! Why would he stay in a place like this when he could be feasting on crayfish with the rest of us? Would you look at him? He's chewing on some rotten, slimy, frogs legs right now. Disgusting!"

"What did you expect after what Notturno told us," said Sirius. "He's probably eating anything that he can find, even if it's been dead for a week. Just look at him, its hard to believe that he's our brother."

The three raccoons decided that it would be wiser not to overwhelm Lepus by approaching him all at once. Procilina and Sirius stayed back and watched from a distance as Orion slowly walked toward Lepus. As Orion drew closer, Lepus ignored him. He didn't seem to notice Orion's presence. He wiped at his nose and scratched at his fur compulsively. Patches of his fur had fallen out revealing the worn skin underneath. Orion took a good look at his tail and saw that the faded black rings had become strangely distorted. As Orion reached a paw out to touch him, Lepus slowly slumped away and started to nod off into a trance-like stupor. Orion began to shake him roughly and Lepus became more alert, but he was not in any mood to see him.

"Go back home Orion. Go away. You don't belong here," grumbled Lepus as he waved him away.

"I didn't come all this way and track you down into this forsaken swamp because I felt like going for a walk Lepus. I came here to bring you back home and I'm not leaving without you. Let's get out of here. Come on Lepus, you don't really want to live like this, do you? Momma is worrying herself sick. It's time for you to come home," said Orion.

"You must be kidding. I'm not going anywhere with you, Orion. I don't care about anybody or anything as long as I get to feed my head," sneered Lepus.

"Feed your head? Your head is messed up. That's what I think, Lepus. Why are you talking this way? Now, you listen to me. You're coming home," said Orion.

"Get lost Orion, can't you see that you're wasting your time?" replied Lepus.

Orion could see that it was useless to try and convince Lepus to leave. He wasn't going to come home voluntarily. He and his brother and sister would have to do something drastic. They would have to force him to leave this miserable place. Watching from a distance, it was obvious to Sirius and Procilina that Orion was getting nowhere. They walked over to where Orion was standing and immediately Lepus became agitated.

"Get lost!" shouted Lepus. "Leave me alone. You don't own me. This is my life, not yours and I'll do whatever I want with it. Don't you get it? When are you jerks gonna figure out that it's useless to try and butt into my schemes. Now, go home!"

"Okay Lepus, we'll leave you alone," said Sirius, "after this!" In an instant, Sirius grabbed Lepus by the scruff of the neck and pulled him to his feet. The skin around his neck was loose and his fur fell out in bunches. It was very hard to get a steady hold of him. With the help of the others, Sirius lifted him up and dragged him away from the stagnant pond and over to a crystal clear pool of still water. Once there, Sirius took a firm hold of his brother and shoved his face close to the water so that he would see his own reflection.

"Take a good look at yourself, Lepus," growled Sirius. "Look at what you've become. You are a disgrace! Look at your face, your faded mask. I've never seen a raccoon with their fur falling out. What have you done to yourself? Look into your eyes, Lepus, and tell me what you see. A dying raccoon, that's what. You've abandoned your life Lepus, but we haven't given up on you yet. We're taking you home whether you like it or not!" Sirius paused for a moment and drew in a deep breath. He continued in a calmer tone. "Come on Lepus, we want to help you. Come with us."

Lepus threw back his head and started flailing his limbs wildly. He cried out with a mournful wail. "Ahheee" Shudders ran through his body and his legs gave out from under him. Sirius tried to steady him as he collapsed, but he lost his grip and couldn't support him. Lepus sprawled on the ground, his ailing body looking as decayed as a heap of dead bones. Procilina ran over to Lepus. She hugged him and cradled his head above the ground. Wrapped in his sister's arms, his body shook with violent tremors. Procilina held him tightly and tried to quell his jittery movements.

Looking down into his masked face she had to muster her courage so that she didn't succumb to her own anguished emotions. In an effort to help, Orion grabbed a wad of tall grass and leaned over him to wipe away the tears and mucus pouring from his watery eyes and runny nose.

A sudden realization had entered the heart of Lepus as he looked down at his reflection in the pool of clear water. The image was hideous and he knew it. The sudden rush of emotion had caused him to almost lose consciousness. His soul had become so corrupted by poison that seeing his own reflection had shocked his heart. His sister could hear him gasping, "Where am I? I'm lost, lost. What happened to me?" Sounds came out of him that none of the others had ever heard before. His moans of agony and despair carried through the Great Forest like the winds of an approaching storm. He sighed and groaned, kicked his legs, and then suddenly went limp. His brothers and sister were dumbfounded. They had never experienced anything like this. They had been warned that Lepus was in terrible shape, but this breakdown was far worse than anything that they had imagined. They had no idea how to deal with such a desperate situation. The three of them looked at each other wide-eyed and together they took a hold of his withered body and began carrying him toward home. Lepus continued to have outbursts as they struggled to drag him through the Great Forest. He slurred his words and mumbled to himself like this:

"I Don't Really Belong"

"I will haunt the forest,
An inch away from dead,
Only Fate can lay to rest,
The voices in my head."

"The dimming of the light,
The Snuffing of the strong,
Forgive me for my flight,
I Don't Really Belong."

CHAPTER
Sixteen

—————————◆►••◄◆—————————

I SUPPOSE THAT IT'S TRUE

A late snow blanketed the Great Forest. A coating of white clung to the trees, weighing down branches until they bowed all the way to the ground. Shrubs had disappeared from view and were little more than mounds of white strewn across the forest floor. Over two feet of snow had fallen on the land, leaving the earth veiled within a frozen wall of silence. The people huddled within their wigwams, seated themselves on top of fur blankets, and filled their wooden bowls with piping hot stew. The descendants of ancient clans gathered together within their long houses as the drifting snow blew to the height of the rooftops. No one would go hungry, despite the massive force of the blizzard, because the people had braids of corn and sacks of food hung from the ceiling. Women worked side by side on a bench covered with woven mats, decorating their clothing with porcupine quills, while the men crafted arrows and spoke of their traps. Only Mapache had ears tuned to hear the slightest rustling of the outside world. He sat stoically in the safety of his wigwam, envisioning the raw beauty of the storm that surrounded him.

Near the shores of the lake, Sign Tracker and his family nestled together, curled up within the hollow of an old oak tree. Their furry coats kept them warm as they drifted off into a deep slumber. They did not eat or drink for days, but instead their bodies fed off the extra fat that they had stored up in the good times. Lepus was leaner than the rest. His mother kept him in her warm embrace, protecting him from the bitterness of the cold air. Procyona's son had been brought home only a week ago, but he had begun to make progress in regaining his health. He had been cooperative so far and she was determined not to let him slip back into his ruinous ways. Exactly what her wayward son had experienced in the darkest corners of the Great Forest she did not know, and it was probably better that way. For the moment, she was satisfied, knowing that he was here with her, surrounded by his family in their favorite tree.

Sign Tracker's family spent several days hidden within the oak tree. When the sun's rays once again lit up the Great Forest, the family roused themselves from their slumber and ventured outside. Lepus was the last to emerge. He peaked out of the tree and squinted his eyes tightly because of the intensity of the glare reflected off the pure white snow. Sign Tracker stayed close to his son and spent a great deal of time trying to distract him from the harmful memories of the past. He focused on ways to guide his son in a better direction. Sign Tracker knew all too well that Lepus needed to build up his strength and develop a purposeful course of action that would draw him away from the things that had harmed him. Above all, his father did not want to enable him to relapse back into his former way of life. He spoke to Lepus about some of his own experiences and how when he was a young raccoon, forces beyond his control had robbed him of his ability to direct his own actions. This loss of freedom, he told his son, was a terrible price to pay. He had found himself entirely driven by destructive impulses. Life had been stolen from him, but with the help of others, he had returned to the land of the living. He and Procyona were willing to do whatever was necessary in order to keep Lepus safe within the family fold. Not knowing for sure where their son had gone and what the future had in store for him filled them with trepidation, but they would never give up the fight to protect their son.

The seasons changed and good times re-entered the life of Lepus. Continuous encouragement and care from his family kept him busy and distracted him from reminders of his misadventures. Eventually, the raccoon parents began to feel more at ease because Lepus seemed to be doing well. He had, in fact, taken a step back so that he could give some thought to his situation with a sober mind. After quite a bit of soul searching he convinced himself that he should stay away from both Alatro and the underground den.

"I can do this," thought Lepus. "I can stay away from Alatro. I'm not gonna have anything more to do with her; or any of those scoundrels out there that are hustling for her. I've gotta turn my life around. Alatro's potion turned me into a fool. It almost killed me! I Quit! I'm done with all that. What I need is a fresh start. I'm leaving my sorrows and regrets behind. As of today, I'm starting over again."

And so it was that Lepus made an earnest decision to make a clean break from Alatro and pull himself out from under the shadows of broken dreams. It wasn't only for himself that he did this, once his heart had been cleansed of the poisons, he had begun to feel guilty about the amount of pain that he had caused his family. Although he was full of good intentions, he would not succeed that easily. He had to stay away from certain places in the Great Forest that would trigger his intense cravings for Alatro's potion. Without self-discipline, purposeful action, and determination he would not stay on the straight path and subdue the impulses that had taken over his life. No doubt, his family would be there to support him, but he would need much more than the support of his family to remain healthy.

Many days Sign Tracker would see his son sitting quietly by himself on the shore of the lake. He would feel a hint of sadness as he kept a watchful eye over his troubled cub. Spellbound by the luminous colors, hovering above the horizon at sunset, Lepus appeared to be lost in a daydream. He would sit awkwardly at first, favoring his leg that had been covered with sores, and then, he would lay down with his bushy ringed tail wrapped loosely around him. As the colors faded and the sky grew dark he would briefly lift his masked face to the sky and then fall back, curling up snugly with his tail covering his nose. After taking a few labored breaths, he would raise himself up again and fix his gaze above the rippling water whispering to himself like this:

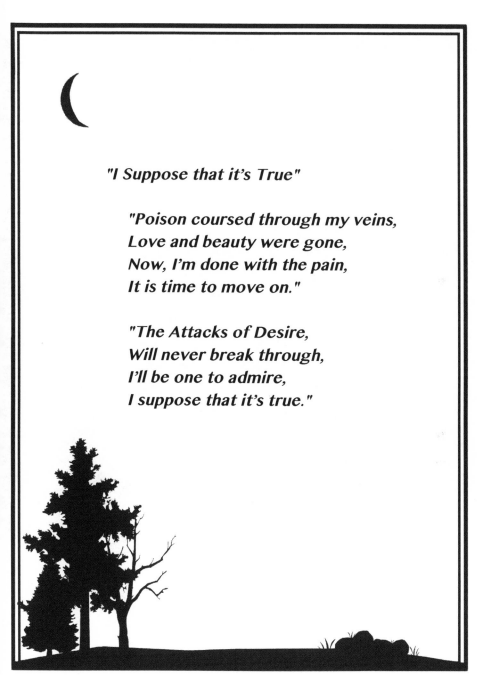

"I Suppose that it's True"

*"Poison coursed through my veins,
Love and beauty were gone,
Now, I'm done with the pain,
It is time to move on."*

*"The Attacks of Desire,
Will never break through,
I'll be one to admire,
I suppose that it's true."*

THE END

Educational Commentary

Sign-Tracking and Drug Addiction

◆·◆·◆·◆·◆·◆·◆·◆·◆·◆·◆·◆

Arthur Tomie & Barbara Zito

I. Introduction

The short stories of The Sign Tracker Trilogy are based on scientific studies of Sign-Tracking as well as on experimental reports detailing the relationship between Sign-Tracking and the drug addiction process. Drug addiction is a widespread problem with many different causes, and no single factor can account for all aspects of this disorder. On the other hand, it is clear that crucial to the prevention of drug addiction is a more thorough understanding of the transition from drug use into drug abuse. The authors conduct research on drug addiction and wrote the stories to explain, particularly to young readers, how drug use can turn into drug abuse and how drug use can continue even when the drug user intends to quit. There are many mysterious aspects to drug addiction, and each of the stories of The Sign Tracker Trilogy communicates to the reader a poorly understood or hidden aspect of the drug addiction process. These secretive aspects of addiction are largely invisible and unrecognized, even after the unsuspecting victim has become trapped in the pitfall of addiction.

II. The Drug Addiction Process

Drug addiction is a serious problem that has ruined the lives of many people. Most of them do not start using drugs with the intention of becoming a drug addict. What usually happens is that people become addicted to drugs even though they believe that they can control their use. Many young people start using drugs only to find out later that their drug-taking has become very difficult to control. Those who experiment with drugs often learn that drug use is easy to start but very difficult to stop.

Drug addiction is a world-wide problem, impacting people of all ages, robbing them of a meaningful, purposeful life. In the beginning, when drug use is initiated, the intent is not to become an out-of-control drug addict. The intent is simply to enjoy the drug's rewarding effects through recreational use of the drug. When drug-taking is voluntary, when it is controlled and managed by the user, then the amount of drug that is taken will be a matter of choice. However, all too often, the use of drugs increases from once a week to several times a week, and is used earlier in the day. Typically, the drugs are taken in larger amounts, resulting in more hits or drinks per episode.

The first hint of a problem is evident when the drug is taken thoughtlessly. The user will sometimes notice that they took the drug automatically, as a matter of habit, without giving it a thought. When drug-taking occurs thoughtlessly, without forming the intention, then the user will experience episodes of excessive drug-taking where the amount of drug consumed is far in excess of the amount intended.

The next step in the evolution of addiction is very troubling. The user will decide that things have gone too far, and that it is time to rein in their drug-taking. Typically, when this happens, the user forms a specific intention to limit their drug use by practicing restraint in the face of temptation. For example, the user may want to restrict the number of drinks for the evening, but after reaching the limit, and despite their intention to hold the line, the user reaches out and has another drink. This is not the same as having a drink absent-mindedly. This is having a drink while resisting the urge to have more. This is a warning sign because it reveals the disconnect between intention (not drinking any more alcohol) and their action (reaching out and drinking more alcohol). It is a blatant violation of free-will and indicates that even though they want to restrain their drug-taking, their intention to do so is meaningless. The disconnect between action and intention reveals that the user is now powerless to control their drug use. At this point, the drug user is well on their way to becoming a drug addict.

Sign-Tracking is a model of drug addiction that reveals the hidden aspects of the drug addiction process. Learning about Sign-Tracking helps us to understand how casual drug use can turn into drug abuse, that is, poorly controlled drug-taking that continues despite the desire to stop. The Sign-Tracking model uses experimental laboratory procedures that resemble some of the experiences encountered during the ritual use of drugs. Fundamental to the model is the rewarding experience that drugs can provide as well as the role of the objects employed to consume abused drugs. Procedures employed in studies of Sign-Tracking induce the performance of Sign-Tracking responses which resemble the poorly controlled actions of the drug addict.

III. The Tail of the Raccoon: Secrets of Addiction

First, a brief review of the first story, "The Tail of the Raccoon: Secrets of Addiction" (Zito & Tomie, 2014) the reader was introduced to the scientific phenomenon of Sign-Tracking, as revealed by the behavior of "Sign Tracker" the raccoon protagonist. In the first story, Sign Tracker agreed to provide Mapache, a blind Native American warrior, with firewood in return for delicious morsels of tasty treats. In the beginning, things went according to plan. The raccoon was very happy to bring firewood to Mapache, because he was thoroughly delighted by the morsels of food he received in reward. However, after many exchanges of firewood for food, the raccoon began to have problems. Strangely, rather than delivering the firewood directly to Mapache, the raccoon began to behave toward the sticks as though they were food, gnawing and chewing on them and dragging the sticks into the lake to be washed. The rubbing and splashing of the sticks, as though they were crayfish, served no purpose, except to delay, sometimes endlessly, the opportunity to eat the foods provided by Mapache. This soon led to serious problems and perplexed all those involved. The raccoon and Mapache were rescued from their predicament by Isquasis, the Native American medicine woman, who nursed the raccoon back to health and instructed him to move to the opposite shore of the Great Lake, away from the food that had such a powerful influence over him. Mapache returned to the village of his people where he entertained the children with his stories about his raccoon friend, the tracker of the sign. And so it was that the raccoon came to be called Sign Tracker.

Educational Commentary

"The Tail of the Raccoon: Secrets of Addiction" is a story about loss of control. Clearly, the raccoon wants to eat Mapache's foods, but, somehow, what he intends to do, which is to gobble up the food, is not what he actually does. Instead, his attention is directed to the sticks, which he gnaws on obsessively. This is because the sticks have become a powerful symbol of reward. The disconnect between the action and the intention of the raccoon is quite puzzling. It is especially difficult to understand the actions of the raccoon because we know that he loves Mapache's food and his Sign-Tracking behavior results in the deterioration of the raccoon's health. Nevertheless, the intention of the raccoon, to devour those tasty treats, is thwarted by his impulse to eat the reward symbol.

The lesson of the story is that there is a disconnect between the intention of the raccoon, to eat the delicious food, and the action of the raccoon, to perform Sign-Tracking, and this disconnect is due to the enormous power of the reward symbol (Breland & Breland, 1961). Sign-Tracking is important because it provides us with a way of understanding how behavior can become irrational and defy free-will. Note that the disconnect between the raccoon's intentions and the raccoon's actions are not unlike those of the drug abuser, who intends to restrain drug-taking, but is unable to control the impulse to have more.

IV. The Tail of the Raccoon, Part II: Touching the Invisible

The role of Sign-Tracking in the drug addiction process is elaborated in greater detail in the second story. This is done by contrasting two instances of Sign-Tracking exhibited by Lepus. Early in the second story, pairings of rope cue with syrup reward lead Lepus to develop Sign-Tracking. Lepus impulsively chews the rope, which is a symbol of reward, causing the rope to fall into the pit, ending all chances of using the rope to retrieve the syrup. Though his Sign-Tracking is counter-productive, Lepus is unable to restrain himself. The Sign-Tracking of Lepus is similar to that which we saw from his father in the first story, in that it reveals the disconnect between action and intention. In this way, we learn that Sign-Tracking behavior is outside of the realm of self-control. It is important to keep this in mind as we consider the second instance of Sign-Tracking behavior exhibited by Lepus later in the second story. This occurs when he experiences the vial paired with Alatro's potion. In this case, the rewarding drug is located inside the vial, which is used to take the drug. Pairings of the vial with the potion lead Lepus to perform Sign-Tracking that is directed at the vial.

What will Sign-Tracking of drug-taking (ST-DT) look like in the case where the rewarding drug potion is located inside the vial cue? When in the presence of the vial, Lepus will find that his eyes are drawn to the vial, which he finds interesting and attractive. Upon seeing the vial, Lepus will become excited and feel the need to move closer to it. Lepus will approach the vial, reach out to touch the vial, grasp the vial, and then drink from the vial. This is Sign-Tracking because the vial signals the rewarding effects of the potion, but in this case, it results in the drinking of the potion located inside the vial. At one point in the second story, Sign-Tracking caused Lepus to consume the potion inside the vial, even when he had decided to limit his use. This was most certainly not a voluntary act of drug-taking. Lepus did not decide to take the drug. Lepus did not intend to take the drug. Lepus was carried along by Sign-Tracking, and so he watched himself thoughtlessly perform a reflexive action that was triggered by the mere presence of the vial. This is Sign-Tracking of drug-taking (ST-DT).

As we learned from the first story, the action of Sign-Tracking is disconnected from intention, so if Lepus attempts to manage his ST-DT, he will surely fail. Lepus is now in the midst of the process of transitioning away from strictly controlled and voluntary drug use. With the emergence of Sign-Tracking, his drug-taking will change so as to include the reflexive and poorly controlled Sign-Tracking form of drug-taking. As the Sign-Tracking form of drug-taking develops, Lepus will find himself, when in the presence of the vial, automatically drinking the potion, even when he did not actually intend to do it. This will lead to bouts of excessive drug-taking. Locating the drug reward inside the reward cue (the object or symbol that precedes the drug's rewarding effects) is the crucial feature of the cue-reward arrangement that results in ST-DT (Tomie & Sharma, 2013).

Note that when humans engage in drug-taking, they typically use an object to aid in consuming the drug (Tomie, 1995). For example, humans drink alcohol from a cocktail glass, snort cocaine through a tooter, or inhale marijuana smoked in a pipe. For humans, the object used to consume the drug will become a drug cue that may come to elicit reflexive Sign-Tracking. Consider, for example, the situation where a person regularly drinks alcohol from a martini glass. Repeated experience with seeing the martini glass just prior to alcohol's rewarding effects will encourage the development of reflexive and impulsive Sign-Tracking of drinking of alcohol from the martini glass. ST-DT occurs when the drug is located inside the object used to consume the drug. Pairings of the object cue with drug reward will induce Sign-Tracking, so that the user will approach the cue, contact the cue, and consume the drug located inside the cue.

V. Sign-Tracking of Drug-Taking (ST-DT) is Invisible

When a person performs an action, that action is usually intended, and we tend to see it as voluntary. For this reason, the development of ST-DT will not stand out because it looks much like ordinary, everyday, intended drug-taking (Tomie, 1995, 1996). Therefore, it is highly likely that to a casual observer, when ST-DT is performed, it will be mistaken for drug-taking that is solely voluntary and intended. This happens because even when ST-DT is performed out in the open and completely visible for all to see, it is well camouflaged, hidden from view by our inclination to automatically attribute drug-taking to personal choice. The lesson of the second story is that when the drug reward is placed inside the object employed to consume the drug, ST-DT will develop. This ST-DT leads to excessive and uncontrolled drug use. Sign-Tracking is the basis of the disconnect between the intention of Lepus to limit his drug intake, and the action of Lepus to perform repeated acts of drug-taking. Despite the obvious evidence of its profound impact, ST-DT remains undetected, invisible, and indiscernible even to the user, because it is readily mistaken for voluntary drug-taking.

Many people who lack an awareness of the existence of Sign-Tracking will likely perceive excessive drug-taking that is due to Sign-Tracking as something that happens because the person is making bad decisions. When we see someone reach out, bring the cocktail glass to their lips, and drink the alcoholic beverage, we assume that the person simply decided to have a drink. We see it that way because, based on our past experiences and in the vast majority of cases, actions do reflect voluntary intention. On the other hand, the extensive scientific literature on Sign-Tracking tells us that the object used to consume the drug will become a drug cue that elicits ST-DT. As we learned from the stories, Sign-Tracking may look like a voluntary action, but Sign-Tracking is actually something quite different. Sign-Tracking is a triggered reflex that is not subject to self-control. ST-DT is camouflaged, making it virtually invisible, and, as such, it is the well-kept secret of the drug addiction process.

Touching the vial when you don't want to, gives good reason to pause, as it is an involuntary action outside the realm of self-control. To those who have no knowledge of Sign-Tracking, the action will most likely be mistaken for and attributed to an act of volition ... something along the lines of ... "I changed my mind." This excuses the behavior, assuages the ego, and allows Sign-Tracking to remain invisible. "Touching the Invisible" describes the behavior of the drug abuser who is blind to Sign-Tracking. The drug abuser who does not see Sign-Tracking can only understand the actions directed at the cue, even those that occur when trying not to do it, as voluntary responses. The act of touching the vial while intending not to do it is perplexing, and requires the concocting of some other explanation, in order to account for the action as an expression of free-will. The goal of this short story is to educate young people about the drug addiction process in a simplified way, and to make people aware of the existence of Sign-Tracking. The purpose of the stories is to provide information that will enable young people to see more clearly the dangers of experimenting with drug use.

VI. Implications of Sign-Tracking

The lesson of the story is that the performance of an action may be involuntary; whether that action is consuming a drug, chewing on a rope, or washing sticks. This behavior can occur automatically and without the involvement of conscious decision-making. Countless drug addicts have said to themselves, "I promised myself not to act that way, but I did it anyway." Drug rehabilitation clinics are filled with recovering addicts who are all too familiar with the feeling of being swept away because they reflexively and automatically reach out and take drugs even though they are desperately trying to resist them.

This story is designed to bring about a better understanding of the phenomenon of Sign-Tracking and to illustrate how a casual drug user can slide so easily into drug addiction. It is clear that many drug addicts are filled with regret and desperately want to quit, but very few are able to do so. The discovery of Sign-Tracking by addiction scientists gives us a clue as to the mystery of why quitting can be extremely difficult, and provides an understanding that sends a clear message to young people that drug use can be dangerous. The story is also intended to provide a better understanding of the problem of drug addiction for family and friends who simply cannot comprehend why their loved ones struggle so mightily to quit drugs. The primary aim of this endeavor is to inform a younger audience of the scientific insights into the dangers of drug use and to add to the arsenal of tools available to those who are dedicated to drug education and prevention of drug abuse. For readers interested in more information about Sign-Tracking and drug addiction, please visit our website: www.tailoftheraccoon.com.

VII. The Tail of the Raccoon, Part III

"The Tail of the Raccoon, Part III", is the third story of The Sign Tracker Trilogy. In Part III, Lepus, though resolved to quit Alatro's potion and live with his family along the shores of the Great Lake, is not entirely free of fond thoughts of the potion's effects. Yet, by removing himself from the vicinity of Alatro's den, and reminding himself of the depths of despair visited upon him by his obsession with the potion,

Lepus makes good on his promise to remain drug-free. Until, that is, he happens upon a chance encounter with Alatro's confederate, who tempts Lepus with a vial of the potion.

Scientific Commentary

Sign-Tracking of Drug-Taking

◆·◆·◆·◆·◆·◆·◆·◆·◆·◆·◆·◆·◆

Arthur Tomie & Barbara Zito

I. Introduction

The short stories of The Sign Tracker Trilogy are based on the scientific phenomenon of Sign-Tracking. The second story, "The Tail of the Raccoon, Part II: Touching the Invisible", depicts the transition from casual and recreational drug use into excessive and poorly controlled drug abuse. This transition comes about due to the development of Sign-Tracking of drug-taking (ST-DT), which is induced by pairings of the object used to consume the drug with the drug's rewarding effects.

II. Sign-Tracking of Drug-Taking (ST-DT)

How does casual drug use encourage the development of ST-DT? Casual drug-taking typically requires an object (cocktail glass, tooter, bong, etc) employed as a conduit to assist in consuming the drug (alcohol, cocaine, marijuana, etc). That object serves as a drug cue because it is paired with the drug reward each time that the drug is consumed. This arrangement is depicted in the story when Lepus experiences the vial just before the rewarding effects of the potion. Repetitions of casual drug-taking, which happen over and over again, expose Lepus to repeated pairings of the vial with the potion. This provides conditions conducive to the emergence of Sign-Tracking responses. Touching the vial, grasping the vial, and consuming the vial are the behaviors of the subject exhibiting Sign-Tracking responses. The vial is the reward cue; therefore, the vial will trigger the reflexive performance of these Sign-Tracking responses, and these Sign-Tracking responses will be directed at the vial. Thus, the Sign-Tracking action sequence will result in the ingestion of the rewarding potion that is located inside the vial cue. The lesson of the second story is that the way to produce the development of ST-DT is to place the potion inside the vial, so that when the potion is consumed through the vial, the user will experience pairings of the vial cue with the rewarding potion. This will encourage the development of Sign-Tracking directed at the vial, as revealed by the consuming of the drug located inside the vial.

Recall that the lesson of the first story was that due to Sign-Tracking there was a disconnect between action and intention. This applies to ST-DT as well. When the drug is consumed through the vial, and ST-DT develops, then the user will experience lack of control of drug-taking. The user will find that they continue to engage in the act of drug-taking even though their intention is to practice restraint. This is portrayed in the second story when Lepus intends to have only one hit, but when in the presence of the vial, his action is to perform repeated acts of drug-taking. In this way, Sign-Tracking contributes to the lack of self-control that leads to episodes where the amount of the drug that is consumed is in excess of that intended.

III. Sign-Tracking of Drug-Taking (ST-DT) is Invisible

Experimental laboratory studies conducted by behavioral scientists have reported that frequency counts of voluntary (i.e., operant or instrumental) responding to obtain reward may actually include Sign-Tracking responses induced by cue-reward pairings. To the naked eye the Sign-Tracking action sequence is indistinguishable from voluntary responding; however, by using experimental manipulations of the cue-reward arrangement, laboratory investigators have provided compelling evidence that cue-reward pairings induce Sign-Tracking responding that looks like and is additive with voluntary operant responding (for reviews, see Hearst and Jenkins, 1974; Schwartz and Gamzu, 1977). It is interesting to note that the convergence of streams of Sign-Tracking responses with streams of voluntary operant responding results in elevated levels of responding that, prior to the discovery of Sign-

Tracking, were mistaken for voluntary acts of reward-directed actions that were performed to excess (Tomie, Brooks, and Zito, 1989). Thus, Sign-Tracking may be camouflaged so as to be mistaken for voluntary responding, and the conditions that produce this masking effect are precisely the same conditions that are employed in drug-taking (Tomie, 1995, 1996). The lesson of the second story is that ST-DT is invisible because, to the naked eye, it passes for voluntary drug-taking. Therein lies the conundrum for the drug abuser, who cannot understand, "Why can't I quit?" The drug abuser can't quit because the action of ST-DT is disconnected from the intention to quit, and their lack of awareness of Sign-Tracking keeps them in the dark. Thus, "Touching the Invisible" describes the behavior of the drug abuser who is blind to the influence of Sign-Tracking.

IV. Scientific Studies of Sign-Tracking Induced by Abused Drugs

There are numerous published scientific reports showing that Sign-Tracking responses develop to an object that signals the delivery of an abused drug. For example, presenting a lever followed by an injection of cocaine induced rats to approach the lever and sniff the lever, even though the cocaine was delivered regardless of what the subject did (Uslaner, Acerbo, Jones, & Robinson, 2006). Other investigators have shown that presenting the lever as a cue for an infusion of cocaine will induce rats to approach the lever and press the lever, even though neither response was necessary to receive the injection of cocaine (Carroll & Lac, 1993; Carroll, Morgan, Lynch, Campbell, & Dess, 2002). Illumination of a light cue above a sipper tube filled with a cocaine solution provided rats with pairings of the light cue with cocaine's rewarding effects, and induced rats to approach the location of the light cue (Di Ciano & Everitt, 2003; Falk & Lau, 1993, 1995), and the rats continued to approach the light cue even when placed at a distance from the cocaine sipper (Falk & Lau, 1993, 1995).

Carroll and Lac (1997) reported that pairing the insertion of a lever with an injection of amphetamine induced rats to press the lever, while other investigators have reported that pairing the insertion of a lever with an injection of heroin induced pressing of the lever (Lynch & Carroll, 1999; Roth, Casimir, & Carroll, 2002). Similar effects are observed with alcohol. Pairing the insertion of a lever with the presentation of a sipper tube filled with alcohol induced rats to press the lever, even though the alcohol sipper was delivered regardless of what the subject did (Tomie, Festa, Sparta, & Pohorecky, 1993). Pairing the brief illumination of a cue light with alcohol drinking induced approach to the location of the cue light (Falk, 1994; Falk & Lau, 1995; Krank, 2003; Krank, O'Neill, Squarey, & Jacob, 2008) and also resulted in elevated performance of an operant drug-seeking response required to obtain access to alcohol drinking (Krank, 2003; Krank, O'Neill, Squarey, & Jacob, 2008). Pairing the intermittent insertion and retraction of a sipper tube filled with alcohol induced elevated alcohol drinking from the sipper tube relative to controls receiving continuous access to the sipper tube filled with alcohol, indicating that the positive correlation between the sipper tube and the alcohol solution induced Sign-Tracking of alcohol drinking (Tomie, Miller, Dranoff, & Pohorecky, 2006; for review see Tomie & Sharma, 2014). Thus, addiction scientists have extensively documented that an object cue that is predictive of drug reward will induce cue-directed Sign-Tracking behavior, and in many of these cases, the performance of Sign-Tracking resulted in elevated drug-taking (Carroll & Lac, 1993, 1997; Carroll, Morgan, Lynch, Campbell, & Dess, 2002; Di Ciano & Everitt, 2003; Falk, 1994; Falk & Lau, 1993, 1995; Krank, 2003; Krank, O'Neill, Squarey, & Jacob, 2008; Lynch & Carroll, 1999; Roth, Casimir, & Carroll, 2002; Tomie, Festa, Sparta, & Pohorecky, 1993; Tomie, Miller, Dranoff, & Pohorecky, 2006; for review see Tomie & Sharma, 2013).

V. Sign-Tracking and Alcohol Drinking in Humans

There is evidence that Sign-Tracking contributes to alcohol drinking in humans (for review, see Tomie & Sharma, 2013). As noted earlier, a container or glassware is typically employed by humans to drink an alcoholic beverage. Drinking from the glassware provides pairings of the glassware with alcohol's rewarding effects, and this may give rise to Sign-Tracking of poorly controlled alcohol drinking. Each pairing of a specific item of glassware, such as a lead crystal stemware cocktail glass, with alcohol's rewarding effects will increase the association between the two. This will increase the likelihood that, when in the presence of that cocktail glass. The association between the cocktail glass and alcohol will be elevated under conditions where alcohol's rewarding effects are always experienced following the cocktail glass, or the cocktail glass is used exclusively for the purpose of consuming an alcoholic beverage. On the other hand, the association between the cocktail glass and alcohol will be reduced when the cocktail glass is employed for purposes other than drinking an alcoholic beverage, or by repeated experience with alcohol's rewarding effects even when the cocktail glass is not present.

There is evidence consistent with the predictions of the Sign-Tracking model. For example, in humans, problem drinking (an indication of poorly controlled alcohol drinking or difficulty in stopping an alcohol drinking episode) is associated with the narrowing of the drinking repertoire (Jellinek, 1960; Cottler, Phelps, and Compton, 1995; McCreary, 2002). This is a style of drinking such that alcohol is only consumed in the form of a favorite alcoholic beverage that is served only in a particular form of glassware. This style of alcohol drinking has been noted to presage the nosological progression into increasingly frequent episodes of excessive and poorly controlled alcohol drinking (Jellinek, 1960). Additional evidence consistent with the Sign-Tracking model is provided by cultural anthropologists who note higher rates of problem drinking in Northern Europe, as compared to Mediterranean Europe, even though the per capita consumption of alcohol in those regions are comparable (deLint, 1973; Heath, 1987). While there are many cultural aspects of alcohol drinking that may contribute to those regional disparities in problem drinking rates, it should be noted that the types of glassware used to consume alcoholic beverages differ across regions and in accordance with predictions of the Sign-Tracking model. North European cultures have widely adopted a style of alcohol drinking such that alcohol is consumed almost exclusively from specialized containers, included lead crystal stemware, goblets, and flutes, as well as metalware in the form of beer mugs and ale steins. This is in contrast to Mediterranean Europe, where alcohol is often consumed from common everyday glassware of the sort also used to consume water or other non-alcoholic beverages (Levin, 1990). These findings suggest that poorly controlled alcohol drinking in humans may be due to Sign-Tracking, and the therapeutic remedies suggested by the model include using common glassware to consume alcoholic beverages and putting way the favorite glassware that have been empowered to trigger Sign-Tracking responses.

VI. Sign-Tracking Confers Vulnerability to Drug Abuse

The second story depicts differences between individuals in the tendency to exhibit Sign-Tracking behavior. The antics of the sons of Sign Tracker reveal that Lepus is more prone than Orion to develop Sign-Tracking. Though the brothers experience the same number of pairings of the rope with the syrup, Orion reacts to rope-syrup pairings in a sensible way, while Lepus reacts quite differently. Due to the pairings of the rope with the syrup, Orion learns that the presence of the rope signals the nearby availability of the syrup. Orion reacts to the information provided by the rope cue, by following the rope to the location of the storage pit. Lepus also learns that the rope is a signal for the nearby availability of the syrup, but reacts in an emotional way to the rope cue. Lepus becomes very excited by the sight of the rope. He is attracted to the rope. He runs to the rope, then licks and chews on the rope, treating the rope as though it were food. Eventually, and much to the dismay of Orion, Lepus becomes so obsessed with eating the rope that he rapidly chews right through it, sending the rope and the sweet treats to the bottom of the pit. Though it's the syrup that Lepus is after, his intention to get at the syrup is thwarted by his actions, which reveal that his obsession with eating the rope, his performance of Sign-Tracking, is outside the realm of his control. Lepus is like his father.

Lepus is a Sign Tracker. Thus, Lepus is unable to control himself when he is in the presence of the reward symbol.

Addiction scientists exploring the relationship between Sign-Tracking and drug addiction have found that the tendency of an individual to develop Sign-Tracking predicts the vulnerability of that individual to drug addiction (Flagel, Akil, & Robinson, 2009; Flagel, Watson, Robinson, & Akil, 2006; Tomie, Grimes, & Pohorecky, 2008). In the addiction science laboratory of Professor Terry Robinson and his associates at the University of Michigan Medical School, a large group of rats were assessed for their tendency to develop Sign-Tracking behaviors in response to the insertion of a lever paired with the delivery of food. Rats that more readily approached and contacted the lever were designated Sign Trackers (ST), while rats that react to the insertion of the lever by approaching the location of food delivery were designated Goal Trackers (GT). All rats are then tested for their tendency to self-administer an abused drug. Each rat was given the opportunity to perform a response that was required in order to receive an injection of an abused drug, such as cocaine, amphetamine, or morphine. ST rats, relative to GT rats, more rapidly acquire the drug-taking response (Beckmann, Marusich, Gipson, & Bardo, 2011), and ST rats, relative to GT rats, take the abused drugs more frequently (Saunders & Robinson, 2010, 2011), moreover, ST rats, relative to GT rats, are more vulnerable to relapse to drug-taking following periods of drug abstinence (Saunders & Robinson, 2010, 2011; for review, see Meyer, Lovic, Saunders, *et al.*, 2012). Thus, vulnerability to Sign-Tracking confers vulnerability to drug addiction.

Scientists are now asking the question, Why are ST rats more addiction-prone than GT rats?" One possible answer lies in the specifics of the experience encountered during the act of drug-taking. To obtain the rewarding effects of the drug, the subject is required to perform a voluntary or operant response, typically called the drug-taking response (sometimes called the drug-seeking response). The drug-taking response is almost invariably an action that is directed at a feature of the environment. Most typically the subject is required to make contact with an object. In doing so, the subject will experience the pairing of that object with the rewarding effects of the drug. As a result of extended training with the drug self-administration procedures, the ST rat, relative to the GT rat, will more likely develop Sign-Tracking directed at the object, resulting in contact with the object. And, contacting the object is programmed to produce an injection of the abused drug. In other words, the specific actions of the drug-taking sequence in the drug self-administration laboratory provide experience that is conducive to the development of Sign-Tracking (Tomie, 1996). It should be noted that drug-taking procedures employed by humans are also conducive to the development of Sign-Tracking (Tomie, 1995). As noted earlier, humans typically employ an object as a conduit to aid in consuming the drug. Humans drink alcoholic beverages from a cocktail glass, snort cocaine through a coke tooter, and use a bong to smoke marijuana. Thus, drug-taking procedures employed by humans are also likely to lead those prone to Sign-Track into developing Sign-Tracking of drug-taking and consequently, prominent symptoms of drug addiction.

Those rats prone to develop Sign-Tracking also exhibit a constellation of other addiction-like behaviors. For example, ST rats tend to be more impulsive than GT rats, taking action quickly and without due consideration of the long term consequences (Lovic, Saunders, Yager, & Robinson, 2011; Tomie, Aguado, Pohorecky, & Benjamin, 1998). ST rats, like human drug addicts, tend to be risk-takers, prone to sensation-seeking and thrill-seeking. In addition, ST rats also tend to respond to novelty with arousal and excitement, rather than with caution (Beckmann, Marusich, Gipson, & Bardo, 2011), and this trait is also observed in humans prone to drug abuse. ST rats also exhibit physiological traits associated with vulnerability to drug abuse (Tomie, Aguado, Pohorecky, & Benjamin, 2000; Tomie, Tirado, Yu, & Pohorecky, 2004; for review, see Tomie, Grimes, & Pohorecky, 2008), as well as neurobiological markers differentially associated with drug addiction (Flagel, Watson, Robinson, & Akil, 2007). Therefore, addiction scientists have concluded that the tendency to perform Sign-Tracking behaviors may be the overt behavioral expression of a personality trait that confers vulnerability to drug addiction (Flagel, Akil, & Robinson, 2009).

It seems ironic that GT rats, even though they are more focused on the reward, are less prone to addiction, while ST rats even though they are more focused on the signal than on the reward, are more vulnerable to becoming addicted (for review, see Meyer, Lovic, Saunders, *et al.,* 2012). Clearly, the attractiveness of the reward cue plays a major role in the drug addiction process (Flagel, Akil & Robinson, 2009; Robinson & Berridge, 1993, 2000; Tomie, Grimes, & Pohorecky, 2008; Tomie & Sharma, 2013).

VII. Sign-Tracking and the Neurobiology of Reward

The experience of a reward is accompanied by an emotional state, often described as a feeling of pleasure, satisfaction, well-being, or euphoria. Scientists have determined that the emotional feelings of euphoria or pleasure are related to activity in an area of the brain called the nucleus accumbens (NAC), which is often called the reward or pleasure center of the brain. The amount of activity in the NAC is determined by the levels of a brain chemical called dopamine. Higher levels of dopamine in the NAC are associated with stronger positive feelings of pleasure. For example, eating food induces the release of dopamine into the NAC, which leads to positive feelings of satisfaction and enjoyment.

Food, water, and sex are natural rewards. Each of these natural rewards produces an increase in DA levels in NAC that produces the positive emotional feelings of pleasure and euphoria. The elevated DA activity in NAC produces other effects as well. For example, any stimuli that happen to be present at the same time or immediately prior to the time that DA NAC activity is elevated by the natural reward are identified and associated with the positive emotional state produced by the natural reward. So, in addition to producing feelings of pleasure, DA activation of NAC also produces connections to stimuli (people, places, things, sounds, etc) that are present at the time of the euphoric episode. The elevated DA activity in NAC also produces an effect on motor responding called psychomotor activation. Thus, natural rewards induce elevated NAC dopamine, which, in turn produces three different types of effects: the emotional feelings of pleasure, the association of stimuli present during the experience of pleasure, and the motor responses of the psychomotor activation syndrome. It is the interplay among these three functions of the integrated reward system, each of which arises from the activation of the NAC, that form the major features of the rewarding experience.

The functional biological significance of the integrated reward system warrants further discussion. Consider the story of the starving beast. An ancient beast is on the verge of starvation. The famished beast picks up a small oblong beige object, looks at it closely, then chews and swallows it. Fortunately, it's a grain of wheat, a food reward that activates the NAC. The reward system kicks into play, automatically giving rise to feelings of pleasure, accompanied by a pattern of motor activity called psychomotor activation. The beast just ate a piece of food, and psychomotor activation is the physical motor activity pattern that automatically follows, to organize the process of looking for more food. Psychomotor activation begins with a survey of the situation, an investigation of the environment, and a search for more food reward. To better investigate the environment, the beast may stand erect, rearing and sniffing, looking around, visually scanning, all the while evaluating the environment for food. But the food is laying on the ground, scattered among stones, dirt, twigs, and other non-food items. Because the grain of wheat was the item that the beast looked at just before NAC activation, this small oblong beige food object is highly likely to be associated by the NAC with strong feelings of pleasure. The association of the grain of wheat with the emotional state of pleasure will improve the chances that the wheat grain will be selected as the target of the psychomotor activation syndrome. The beast locates on the ground nearby another small brown oblong object. It's another grain of wheat. Psychomotor activation automatically leads the beast to approach the grain of wheat, pick up the grain of wheat, and eat the grain of wheat. After eating the second grain of wheat, the beast feels another jolt of pleasure, which is experienced right after seeing the grain of wheat, resulting in even more of an association between the wheat grain and feelings of pleasure. In this way, each grain of wheat becomes more tightly associated with pleasure, making the beast increasingly likely to approach, contact, and eat the wheat. Note that the beast is saved from starving by the integrated functions of the reward system (pleasure, association, psychomotor activation). Note also that for this beast, the process of directing eating responses at food was largely automatic, conferring on this individual beast more of a chance of surviving in a patchy world of scarce food resources. The beast survives, increasing the chances of reproductive success, and transmitting this trait, the integrated reward system, to successive generations of progeny. Evolution has equipped the brain of modern beasts with the integrated reward system, deployed upon activation of NAC, to aid in survival. When we experience reward, we experience the emotion of pleasure, the association of the pleasure with stimuli present at that time, and the psychomotor activation pattern of responding.

Drugs of abuse, such as alcohol, cocaine, and opiates, all activate the same NAC reward system that is activated by natural rewards such as food, water, and sex, but the magnitude of the activation of the NAC by abused drugs may be many times greater than the effect produced by natural rewards. In this way, drugs of abuse hijack the reward system, diverting the system away from the subserving of survival, toward the subserving of addictive behavior.

How the integrated reward system subserves addictive behavior warrants further discussion. Consider the story of Johnny having a drink. Johnny is a moderate, social drinker. He enjoys having a few beers with his friends typically on the weekend. Lately, however, he has noticed that his beer intake has been gradually increasing, so that instead of having two beers at the poker game, he drinks four beers, or more. Drinking beer is pleasurable and mood-improving because the alcohol in the beer produces elevated DA activity in the NAC. In addition, activation of the NAC leads Johnny to associate other stimuli present at that time with these positive emotional feelings, so that Johnny feels good around his drinking pals. The NAC associates the people, places, and things, including sounds, like music, present while drinking beer, with the positive feelings of beer-induced euphoria. We should note that the stimulus that is most closely associated with the DA activation of the NAC is the beer bottle. This is because the beer bottle is seen in the moments in time just before the beer is consumed. The association between the beer bottle and the activation of DA in the NAC will cause the beer bottle to become the target of the psychomotor activation syndrome. This means that Johnny will notice the beer bottle. It conspicuously stands out. Johnny will also find that he is drawn toward the beer bottle. He will reach out and take the beer bottle in his hands, hold the beer bottle, and then drink from it. But the beer consumed due to the psychomotor activation syndrome is not the same as the beer that is consumed as a voluntary, controlled response. The psychomotor activation syndrome is a reflex coming out of the activation of the NAC. Psychomotor activation is not an intended action. Johnny did not decide to drink some more beer. Johnny is drinking beer on automatic pilot. In this way, the integrated reward system leads to beer drinking that occurs but was not intended or subject to self-control. Obviously, beer drinking beyond what is intended is outside the realm of free-will and will be difficult, if not impossible, to manage. Due to alcohol's effects on dopamine levels in NAC, alcohol use can occur even though you do not intend to have a drink. And, the more you drink, the more likely the psychomotor activation syndrome will produce unintended alcohol drinking. In summary, the neurobiological basis of reward and addiction, as revealed by the functions of the integrated reward system (pleasure, association, and psychomotor activation), coincides remarkably with the features of Sign-Tracking.

VIII. The Tail of the Raccoon, Part III

"The Tail of the Raccoon, Part III", is the third story of The Sign Tracker Trilogy. In Part III, Lepus, though resolved to quit Alatro's potion and live with his family along the shores of the Great Lake, is not entirely free of fond thoughts of the potion's effects. Yet, by removing himself from the vicinity of Alatro's den, and reminding himself of the depths of despair visited upon him by his obsession with the potion, Lepus makes good on his promise to remain drug-free. Until, that is, he happens upon a chance encounter with Alatro's confederate, who tempts Lepus with a vial of the potion.

References:

Beckmann, J. S., Marusich, J. A., Gipson, C. D., & Bardo, M.T. (2011). Novelty seeking, incentive salience and acquisition of cocaine self-administration in the rat. *Behavioural Brain Research, 216*, 159-65.

Breland, K., & Breland, M. (1961). The misbehavior of organisms. *American Psychologist, 16*, 681.

Carroll, M. E., & Lac, S. T. (1993). Autoshaping i.v. cocaine self-administration in rats: effects of nondrug alternative reinforcers on acquisition. *Psychopharmacology, 110*, 5-12.

Carroll, M. E., & Lac, S. T. (1997). Acquisition of i.v. amphetamine and cocaine self-administration in rats as a function of dose. *Psychopharmacology, 129*, 206-14.

Carroll, M. E., Morgan, A. D., Lynch, W. J., Campbell, U. C., & Dess, N. K. (2002). Intravenous cocaine and heroin self-administration in rats selectively bred for differential saccharin intake: phenotype and sex differences. *Psychopharmacology, 161*, 304-13.

Cottler, L. B., Phelps, D. L., & Compton, W. M., III. (1995). Narrowing of the drinking repertoire criterion: should it have been dropped from ICD-10? *Journal of Studies of Alcohol, 56*, 173-176.

deLint, J. (1973). The epidemiology of alcoholism: The exclusive nature of the problem, estimating the prevalence of excessive alcohol use and alcohol-related mortality, current trends and the issue of prevention. Toronto: Addiction Research Foundation of Ontario.

Di Ciano, P., & Everitt, B. J. (2003). Differential control over drug-seeking behavior by drug-associated conditioned reinforcers and discriminative stimuli predictive of drug availability. *Behavioral Neuroscience, 117*, 952-960.

Falk, J. L. (1994). The discriminative stimulus and its reputation: Role in the instigation of drug abuse. *Experimental and Clinical Psychopharmacology, 2*, 43-52.

Falk, J. L., & Lau, C. E. (1993). Oral cocaine as a reinforcer: acquisition conditions and importance of stimulus control. *Behavioural Pharmacology, 4*, 597-609.

Falk, J. L., & Lau, C. E. (1995). Stimulus control of addictive behavior: persistence in the presence and absence of a drug. *Pharmacology, Biochemistry, and Behavior, 50*, 71-5.

Flagel, S. B., Akil, H., & Robinson, T. E. (2009). Individual differences in the attribution of incentive salience to reward-related cues: Implications for addiction. *Neuropharmacology, 56*, 139-148.

Flagel, S. B., Watson, S. J., Robinson, T. E., & Akil, H. (2006). An animal model of individual differences in "conditionability": relevance to psychopathology. *Neuropsychopharmacology, 31*, S262-S263.

Flagel, S. B., Watson, S. J., Robinson, T. E., & Akil, H. (2007). Individual differences in the propensity to approach signals vs goals promote different adaptation in the dopamine system of rats. *Psychopharmacology, 191*, 599-607.

Hearst, E., Jenkins, H. M. (1974). Sign-tracking: The stimulus-reinforcer relation and directed action. Austin, TX: Psychonomic Society.

Heath, D. B. (1987). Anthropology and alcohol studies: Current issues. *Annual Review of Anthropology, 16*, 99-120.

Jellinek, E. M. (1960). Alcoholism, a genus and some of its species. *Canadian Medical Association Journal, 83*, 1341-1345.

Krank, M. D. (2003). Pavlovian conditioning with ethanol: sign-tracking (autoshaping), conditioned incentive, and ethanol self-administration. *Alcoholism: Clinical and Experimental Research, 27,* 1592-1598.

Krank, M. D., O'Neill, S., Squarey, K., & Jacob, J. (2008). Goal- and signal-directed incentive: conditioned approach, seeking, and consumption established with unsweetened alcohol in rats. *Psychopharmacology, 196,* 397-405.

Levin, J. D. (1990). *Alcoholism: A Biopsychosocial Approach.* New York: Hemisphere Publishing Corp.

Lovic, V., Saunders, B.,T., Yager, L. M., & Robinson, T. E. (2011). Rats prone to attribute incentive salience to reward cues are also prone to impulsive action. *Behavioural Brain Research, 223,* 255-261.

Lynch, W. J., & Carroll, M. E. (1999). Sex differences in the acquisition of intravenously self-administered cocaine and heroin in rats. *Psychopharmacology, 144,* 77-82.

McCreary, D. R. (2002). Binge drinking in adulthood: the influence of gender, age, and beverage exclusivity. *International Journal of Men's Health, 1,* 233-245.

Meyer, P. J., Lovic, V., Saunders, B. T., , *et al.* (2012). Quantifying individual variation in the propensity to attribute incentive salience to reward cues. *PLoS One, 7,* e38987.

Robinson, T. E., & Berridge, K. C. (1993). The neural basis of drug craving: An incentive sensitization theory of addiction. *Brain Research Reviews, 18,* 247-291.

Robinson, T. E., & Berridge, K. C. (2000). The psychology and neurobiology of addiction: an incentive-sensitization view. *Addiction, 95 (Suppl.),* S91-117.

Roth, M. E., Casimir, A. G., & Carroll, M. E. (2002). Influence of estrogen in the acquisition of intravenously self-administered heroin in female rats. *Pharmacology, Biochemistry, and Behavior, 72*, 313-318.

Saunders, B. T., & Robinson, T. E. (2010). A cocaine cue acts as an incentive stimulus in some but not others: implications for addiction. *Biological Psychiatry, 67*, 730-736.

Saunders, B. T., & Robinson, T. E. (2011). Individual variation in the motivational properties of cocaine. *Neuropsychopharmacology, 34*, 1668-1676.

Schwartz, B., & Gamzu, E. (1977). Pavlovian control of operant behavior: An analysis of autoshaping and its implications for operant conditioning (pp. 53-97). In: Honig, W. K., Staddon, J. E. R., Eds. *Handbook of operant behavior*. Englewood Cliffs, NJ: Prentice-Hall.

Tomie, A. (1995). CAM: An animal learning model of excessive and compulsive implement-assisted drug-taking in humans. *Clinical Psychology Reviews, 15*, 145-167.

Tomie, A. (1996). Locating reward cue at response manipulandum (CAM) induces symptoms of drug abuse. *Neuroscience & Biobehavioral Reviews, 20*, 505-535.

Tomie, A., Aguado, A. S., Pohorecky, L. A., & Benjamin, D. (1998). Ethanol induces impulsive-like responding in a delay-of-reward operant choice procedure: impulsivity predicts autoshaping. *Psychopharmacology, 139*, 376-382.

Tomie, A., Aguado, A. S., Pohorecky, L. A., & Benjamin, D. (2000). Individual differences in pavlovian autoshaping of lever pressing in rats predict stress-induced corticosterone release and mesolimbic levels of monoamines. *Pharmacology, Biochemistry, and Behavior, 65*, 509-517.

References

Tomie. A., Brooks, W., & Zito, B. (1989). Sign-tracking: The search for reward. In S. Klein, S. and R. Mowrer (Eds.), *Contemporary Learning Theories: Pavlovian Conditioning and the Status of Traditional Learning Theory*, pp. 191-223. Lawrence Erlbaum Associates, Hillsdale, NJ.

Tomie, A., Festa, E. D., Sparta, D. R., & Pohorecky, L. A. (2003). Lever conditioned stimulus-directed autoshaping induced by saccharin-ethanol unconditioned stimulus solution: effects of ethanol concentration and trial spacing. *Alcohol, 30*, 35-44.

Tomie, A., Grimes, K. L., & Pohorecky, L.A. (2008). Behavioral characteristics and neurobiological substrates shared by Pavlovian sign-tracking and drug abuse. *Brain Research Reviews, 58*, 121-135.

Tomie, A., Miller, W. C., Dranoff, E., & Pohorecky, L. A. (2006). Intermittent presentations of ethanol sipper tube induce ethanol drinking in rats. *Alcohol and Alcoholism, 41*, 225-230.

Tomie, A., & Sharma, N. (2013). Pavlovian Sign-Tracking Model of alcohol abuse. *Current Drug Abuse Reviews, 6*, 201-219.

Tomie, A., Tirado, A. D., Yu, L., & Pohorecky, L. A. (2004). Pavlovian autoshaping procedures increase plasma corticosterone and levels of norepinephrine and serotonin in prefrontal cortex in rats. *Behavioural Brain Research, 153*, 97-105.

Uslaner, J. M., Acerbo, M. J., Jones, S. A., & Robinson, T. E. (2006). The attribution of incentive salience to a stimulus that signals an intravenous injection of cocaine. *Behavioural Brain Research, 169*, 320-324.

Zito, B., & Tomie, A. (2014). *The Tail of the Raccoon: Secrets of Addiction.* . Paperback, Createspace, 70 pages. Princeton, NJ: ZT Enterprises, LLC.

Glossary

Affinity: A natural liking or attraction; similarity; connection.

Astray: Away from the correct path or direction; lost.

Bedazzle: Greatly impress (someone) with brilliance or skill; make oblivious to faults or shortcomings.

Bedraggle: To make limp and soiled as with rain or dirt.

Buffet: Strike repeatedly and violently; batter.

Cache: A collection of items of the same type stored in a hidden place.

Chivalrous: Courteous, considerate, and gallant, especially toward women.

Concoction: A mixture of various ingredients or elements.

Consort: To associate with a partner, socialize, keep company.

Coy: Shy; modest; to show reluctance.

Desirous: To want, wish, or long for something that brings satisfaction or enjoyment; having or characterized by desire.

Dexterous: Demonstrating nimble skill, implying quickness and ease of performance, especially with hands.

Dissuade: Persuade (someone) not to take a particular course of action.

Dullard: Slow or stupid.

Enshroud: Envelop completely and hide from view.

Escapade: An act or incident involving excitement, daring, or adventure.

Foreboding: Fearful apprehension; a feeling that something bad will happen.

Grovel: Humble oneself as in fear or submission; lie or move abjectly on the ground with one's face downward.

Gullible: Easily persuaded to believe something.

Haunches: Hindquarters; leg and loin of an animal.

Impetuous: Acting or done quickly and without thought or care.

Incessant: Without interruption; constant.

Inexplicable: Unable to be explained or accounted for.

Inquisitive: Curious, given to asking questions, eager for knowledge.

Interloper: A person who becomes involved in a place or situation where they are not wanted or considered not to belong.

Loll: To hang loosely; sit, lie, or lean in a lazy, relaxed way.

Luminous: Full of or radiating light; shining, especially in the dark.

Meander: To walk aimlessly.

Mesmerize: Hold the attention of someone to the exclusion of all else; hypnotize; captivate.

Nostalgic: Yearn for the happiness of a former place or time; sentimental, romantic feelings.

Obliterate: Total destruction, remove all traces of, do away with.

Ominous: Give the impression that something bad or unpleasant is going to happen; threatening.

Pacify: Restore to a state of peace; appease; quell anger, agitation, or excitement.

Palisade: A fence of wooden stakes or iron railings fixed in the ground, forming an enclosure or defense.

Plummet: Fall or drop straight down at high speed.

Quiver: Tremble or shake with slight rapid motion.

Quizzical: Mild puzzlement; questioning of something odd or strange.

Rawhide: Stiff untanned leather.

Silhouette: The dark shape, image, or outline of something visible against a light background, especially in dim light.

Slacken: Loose, release, relax.

Sonorous: Giving out an imposingly deep, full, and resonant sound.

Subside: Become less intense, less active, or severe.

Tantalize: Tease (someone) with the sight or promise of something that is out of reach or unobtainable.

Torrential: Falling rapidly, unceasingly, and abundantly; in large quantities, especially rain or water.

Trepidation: A feeling of fear or agitation about something that may happen.

Uncanny: Seemingly beyond the ordinary; strange or mysterious.

Vantage: A place or position affording a good view of something.

Venerable: Commanding a great deal of respect, especially because of age, wisdom, or character; impressive dignity; worthy of reverence.

Venison: Deer meat used for food.

Vigil: A period of keeping awake during the normal hours of sleep, especially to keep watch or pray.

Wistful: Silently attentive in a sad way; longing, yearning.

48021135R00108

Made in the USA
Charleston, SC
22 October 2015